PRÉCIS OF SPECIAL RELATIVITY

PRÉCIS OF
SPECIAL RELATIVITY

O. Costa de Beauregard

Institut Henri Poincaré
Paris, France

Translated by Banesh Hoffmann

Queens College
The City University of New York
Flushing, New York

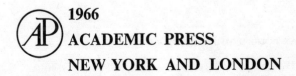

1966
ACADEMIC PRESS
NEW YORK AND LONDON

ACADEMIC PRESS INC.
111 Fifth Avenue, New York, New York 10003

United Kingdom Edition published by
ACADEMIC PRESS INC. (LONDON) LTD.
Berkeley Square House, London W.1

LIBRARY OF CONGRESS CATALOG CARD NUMBER: 66-25515

PRINTED IN THE UNITED STATES OF AMERICA

PREFACE TO THE ENGLISH EDITION

To do long division with Roman numerals is possible but it is not easy. To analyze the physical phenomena without using the full language of four dimensions is also possible, but offers neither depth of insight nor swiftness of analysis nor beauty of result. Today it has more widely come to be realized that nature derives its entire way of action from the four-dimensional character of space-time. One recognizes that the simplest description of the separation between two events is furnished, not by their separation in time, but by the so called "interval" between. To adopt a mathematician's language, one comes to think of the vectorial separation between the two events in space and time as more deeply significant than any of the components of this vector. Similarly one comes to realize that there is a deeper unity than energy and momentum, a vectorial quantity whose components can be viewed in one or another reference frame but which has a meaning quite apart from all arbitrariness in the choice of an inertial reference system.

The space-time point of view today—ten years after Einstein's death, fifty years after the enunciation of general relativity, and sixty years after special relativity—has become as natural a part of the thinking of the student of physics as Euclidean geometry was to the student of an earlier age. Its perspectives provide indispensable working tools.

For those who will have to work with these tools, this book by O. Costa de Beauregard offers unusual depth of insight. I know of no book that is at the same time more precise, more accurate, and more succinct in presenting so complete a treatment of Special Relativity. Because of the clarity of the exposition this book is truly accessible to the student of physics.

August, 1966   JOHN ARCHIBALD WHEELER

PREFACE TO THE FRENCH EDITION

This little précis has been extracted, in both overall plan and technical details, from our treatise *La Théorie de la Relativité Restreinte*, published by Masson (Paris) in 1949.

In making the condensation, we had to choose between the basic explanations and the details of the calculations. We have taken the view that the goal to be reached is a genuine understanding of a theory which, though no longer difficult, remains nevertheless elusive so long as one does not penetrate to its spirit. We have therefore not been niggardly of the explanations, but have often presented them almost as fully here as in our treatise. It is to the details of the calculations that we have applied the ax: we present them in full outline rather than in full. The reader who wishes to learn more about them can consult our treatise or any of the excellent works on the theory, a partial list of these books being given in the bibliography.

On some points we have improved the presentation by using ideas that have come to us, or that we have come upon, since the publication of our previous work.

O. COSTA DE BEAUREGARD

CONTENTS

CHAPTER 4 RELATIVISTIC DYNAMICS

CHAPTER 5 ANALYTICAL DYNAMICS

NOTATION

Throughout this book indices u, v, w will refer to the spatial axes 1, 2, 3, and i, j, k, l to the indices of the space-time axes 1, 2, 3, 4. Three-dimensional vectors of ordinary space will be printed in bold face.

The numbers of the sections of the five chapters are denoted by 1.1, 1.2, etc., and those of the equations by (1-1), (1-2), etc. The number before the period or hyphen is omitted in internal references within a chapter.

PRÉCIS OF SPECIAL RELATIVITY

Chapter 1

INTRODUCTION

A. The Special Principle of Relativity

1.1 The Principle of Relativity in the Kinematics and Dynamics of Galileo and Newton

When Einstein and Minkowski forced us to re-examine the whole problem of the *principle of relativity*, it became clear that the status of this principle in the dynamics of Galileo and Newton was by no means free of paradox. Newton had said that his system rested on the two concepts of *absolute space* and *universal time*, and for him the idea of absolute space signified not only that the set of points constituting space was independent of the motion of the reference frame, but also that there existed a particular rigid three-dimensional reference frame that could be considered to be at rest in an absolute sense.

The development of classical kinematics and dynamics showed this last assertion to be merely verbal or, if we prefer, nonoperational.

Classical mechanics associates with Euclidean geometry a parameter t representing "absolute time," and then "for each instant" uses transformations of variables of the form

$$\bar{x}^u = \bar{x}^u(x^1, x^2, x^3, t), \qquad u = 1, 2, 3, \qquad (1\text{-}1)$$

1

which, by hypothesis, leave the square of the spatial distance invariant. In particular, we can confine ourselves to transformations of orthogonal axes, namely transformations of the form

$$\bar{x}^u = \sum_{v=1}^{3} O^u_v(t) x^v \equiv O^u_v(t) x^v, \qquad (1\text{-}2)$$

where the $O^u_v(t)$ are the coefficients of a *linear orthogonal substitution*.[1] We have just introduced *en passant* Einstein's summation convention on dummy indices, according to which every index appearing twice in a monomial, once as a superscript and once as a subscript[2] is *automatically* to be summed over all its possible values; the explicit expression for the third term in (2) is given by the second. Since the *Einstein summation convention* is imposed right at the start in the tensor calculus, we shall use it here throughout.

If x^u and $\bar{x}^u$ are two trihedrals in Euclidean space that are Cartesian in the strict sense, formulas (2) and their inverses (which are of the same form) express the *principle of relative motion* of classical kinematics. According to this principle, the set of points constituting Euclidean space is independent of the motion of the reference frame (though this will no longer be the case in Einstein's theory). Moreover, *all three-dimensional Cartesian reference frames in space, no matter what their relative motions, even if these be accelerated or rotating, are considered to be equivalent for the description of motion*. For example, the system of axes at rest relative to the platform of a station, the system at rest relative to the accelerating train, the system at rest relative to the village square, and the system at rest relative to a merry-go-round, all are counted as *kinematically* equivalent in the "rational mechanics" of Galileo and Newton.

---

[1] See §§8 and 9 for a more detailed treatment of linear orthogonal substitutions.

[2] See §7 for the "covariant" and "contravariant" significance of subscripts and superscripts.

As we shall see, *Einstein, in propounding his new universal special principle of relativity, will reject the principle of an absolute reference frame in space as too narrow and the principle of relative motion as too broad. His new principle will be at the same intermediate level as the principle of relativity of classical dynamics. Like the latter it will affirm the privileged equivalence of a special class of spatial, three-dimensional reference frames, all in uniform translation with respect to one another.*

It is well known that the dynamics of Galileo and Newton denies the existence of an absolute reference frame in space so far as dynamics is concerned, but affirms the absolute character of the translational or rotational accelerations of the reference frame. The theory leads to the appearance of both linear inertial forces and angular inertial forces (Coriolis forces) whose existence is fully verified by experiment. From this new point of view, the reference frames at rest relative to the station platform and the village square are privileged compared with those carried along by the accelerating train and the merry-go-round. This will also be the point of view of *the special theory of relativity,* but there it will apply *even in kinematics.*

1.2 The Principle of Relativity and Optics

If one applies the classical concepts of kinematics to optics one is almost inevitably led to assume the existence of an absolute reference frame in space. For, suppose that in a certain reference frame the speed of light waves is isotropic and has the value c; and consider, for example, spherical waves emanating from a source O at rest in this reference frame. Then in a reference frame moving with speed v relative to the first, the classical law of composition of velocities predicts that the speed of the waves will vary, according to direction, between the values $c+v$ and $c-v$.

From Arago (1818) to Michelson and Morley (1887) the classical physicists had performed a considerable number of experiments, conceived in terms of the above scheme, in order to exhibit this absolute reference frame of space. They firmly believed in its existence, and gave it materiality more or less (or rather, less and less) under the name *ether*.

The results of all these experiments have been negative.[3]

Arago, in 1818, inaugurated the series of *experiments of the first order in* $\beta = v/c$ when he let light from a star pass through a prism. Contrary to his expectations, he found that the deviation is the same as when the source is fixed on the earth. Though this experiment was historically extremely important and led Fresnel to his law of composition of velocities in optics, it was not ideally pure in principle. Since it involved a relative velocity of the source and the receiver, one ought to introduce explicitly the concept of the Doppler effect, which was actually not formulated till 24 years later! But Ångström, and then Mascart (1872), repeated Arago's experiment in purified form with source and receiver both attached to a single optical bench, and using respectively a prism and a grating as the dispersive device. They found that the measured deviation is independent of the orientation of the optical bench.

This Ångström–Mascart type of experiment amounts essentially to counting, in a static situation, the number of waves in propagation along the length of a material rod and of verifying that, to the first order in $\beta = v/c$, this number is independent of the orientation of the rod. If the dispersive apparatus is a grating, the waves never travel in glass and one has to apply the theory of the Doppler effect twice (at emission and at reception). *It is most remarkable that when one makes this calcu-*

---

[3] The illustrious Fizeau believed he had found a positive result for the rotation of the plane of polarization of light passing through a pile of glass plates, but the same experiment repeated by Brace (1905) and by Strasser (1907) gave a negative result.

lation using the classical law of composition of velocities one finds that the so-called absolute velocity v of the experimental apparatus disappears to the first order in $\beta = v/c$, which is precisely the mathematical translation of the experimental result.

If the dispersive apparatus is a prism, the waves travel a sizeable distance in a medium of refractive index $n > 1$, as in Arago's original experiment. It was in this connection that Fresnel demonstrated his cleverness by producing a "made to measure" formula to account for the negative result of the experiment: his *law of the longitudinal dragging of light waves by material media* of refractive index n, according to which the observed velocity, c', of the waves has the value

$$ c' = \frac{c}{n} \pm v\left(1 - \frac{1}{n^2}\right). \tag{1-3} $$

This formula was verified in the laboratory by Fizeau (1851), Michelson (1886), and Zeeman (1914).

What is remarkable about Fresnel's ether drag law, as Potier pointed out in 1874, is that *it has to do with a universal law of composition of the velocity c/n of waves relative to a medium and the velocity v of the medium itself* (regarded as absolute).

With Stokes (1851), Mascart (1872), and Veltmann (1873), Potier extracts from Fresnel's law a consequence of great importance both technically and historically: he shows that *Fresnel's ether drag law implies the absence of all effects of the ether wind to the first order in* $\beta = v/c$. (Incidentally, Fresnel himself had remarked that his formula is of the first order in β.) What had already been known for the vacuum was thus extended to refractive media.

Because of the results of Stokes, Mascart, Veltmann, and Potier, Michelson performed an experiment of the second order in $\beta = v/c$. The details of his experiment are to be found in all treatises on optics and we shall not pause to give them here. Let us say briefly that the Michelson–Morley experiment (1887) consisted in comparing by means of an interferometer the numbers of standing waves of light carried by two perpendicular material rods and demonstrating that the ratio of these numbers is independent of the orientation of the apparatus. One concludes from this that the number of standing waves of light carried by a given material rod is independent of the orientation of the rod. And this time the conclusion is obtained to the second order in β.

It amounts to the same thing to say that the speed of light on a there-and-back journey, when measured by a material standard of length and by a standard of time that is the period of the radiation being used, is independent of the orientation of the rod. *Since this result is established to the second order in* $\beta = v/c$, *it is incompatible with the classical law of composition of velocities.*

Such, at least, is the conclusion that Einstein drew in 1905. Immediately after the Michelson–Morley experiment, Fitzgerald (cited by Lodge) and Lorentz responded (as Fresnel had earlier to the experiment of Arago) with a hypothesis and a formula tailored *ad hoc*, namely those of the *longitudinal contraction of material bodies in an ether wind* according to a certain universal law that we shall soon obtain.

What was epistemologically vicious in the hypothesis of Fitzgerald and Lorentz, as also in that of Fresnel, is that it affirmed simultaneously the existence of the *ether* and the impossibility of bringing it into evidence experimentally. This was a negation of the rule that in physics everything ought to be operational, that the discussion should be tailored to the measure of the formalism revealed by experiment. And since the Fresnel and Fitzgerald–Lorentz hypotheses were really *universal laws* independent of the type of matter of which the test body was made and involving only the velocities, the fact is that in the last analysis they had to do with a problem of kinematics.

And the problem had indeed been thus posed (identification

of the hypothesis of an *ether* with that of an absolute reference frame in space). What had not been understood at first was how closely optics is physically linked to geometry, to chronometry, and to kinematics: the fundamental quantities of optics are, in fact, lengths (the wavelengths), times (the periods), and pure numbers (the phases).

1.3   The Principle of Relativity and Group Theory

With the piling up of "negative experiments" in optical kinematics, initially to the first order in $\beta = v/c$, and then to the second, many physicists (notably Mascart and Poincaré) came to believe that the *principle of relativity* of dynamics (the privileged equivalence of Galilean reference frames) must be a general law of physics, and in particular of optics.

If this were the case, the historical distinction between effects of the first and second order in β would not in itself have the importance that the accident of events had bestowed on it. The true problem would be to seek the group of the transformations linking the various Galilean frames.

Indeed, following von Laue,[4] we shall derive the formulas of the Lorentz–Poincaré group in their four-dimensional form by making use of the invariance of the value of c in accordance with the result of the Michelson–Morley experiment. The new interpretation of the *Lorentz contraction* as *reciprocal* and *relative* will then emerge of its own accord.

But we have insisted on the similar status of Fresnel's ether-drag law with respect to effects of the first order and the Lorentz contraction with respect to those of the second order. Because of Potier's demonstration, it became customary to consider classical kinematics *together with* Fresnel's law, on the one hand,

---

[4] *Ann. Physik* **23,** 989 (1907).

and relativistic kinematics, on the other, to be equivalent as far as the first order in β. This, however, is a dubious point of view since classical kinematics does not use Fresnel's law (for small v) as the formula of infinitesimal transformation of a group, while in relativistic kinematics this formula is none other than the law of composition of velocities, which of course belongs to a group (von Laue, 1907). Abelé and Malvaux, in 1954, established the reciprocal property: assuming that Fresnel's ether-drag law is the infinitesimal formula of a group, they deduced the Lorentz–Poincaré formulas (see §2.8). In other words, and contrary to a view that has long been prevalent, *the negative effect of the first order in β suffices to establish relativistic kinematics, provided one adds the postulate of a group structure.*

1.4   First Order Effects in β and the Measurement of the Speed of Light on a One-Way Journey

The optical effects of the first order in β are essentially the Doppler effect (1842), which is a longitudinal effect, and Bradley's aberration (1728), which is a transverse effect: all other effects can be regarded as a combination of these two. Formally speaking, the Doppler effect is identical with the Römer effect (1676), where the period of the eclipses of a satellite of Jupiter played the role of the emission period of the waves.

As we have said, the Doppler effect and Bradley's aberration have in common that, to the first order, the absolute velocities of the source and the receiver cancel out in such a way that only their relative velocity remains. Because of this, although classical and relativistic kinematics are numerically equivalent in their description of effects *of the first order,* the latter is much more satisfactory in that it does not introduce something that is un-observable.

The Römer–Doppler effect on the one hand, and the Bradley

effect on the other, have the interesting property that they permit the measurement of the speed of light on a one-way journey. The price for this is that the relative velocity of source and receiver must vary in a known manner. Historically it was precisely the Römer and Bradley effects that gave the first evaluations of the constant c (the speed of light in a vacuum). The modern methods of measuring c (of which we shall speak later) are much more precise; the use of the Doppler effect however is still of interest: even today it provides the means for determining the velocity of the earth in its orbit in terms of the astronomical second and the standard meter, and out of this comes the determination of the dimensions of the ecliptic, and thus of the parsec in terms of the meter.

1.5 The Michelson–Morley Experiment. Optical Measurement of Length. Hertzian Chronometry. Measurement of c

We have perhaps not sufficiently emphasized that *metrological comparisons of a material length such as the standard meter and the length of a standing wave of light* (experiments of Michelson and Benoit, 1893; Pérot, Fabry, and Benoit, 1906; etc.) *logically presuppose* the negative result of the Michelson–Morley experiment. Indeed, if this result had not been negative, every metrological comparison of the above sort would logically have to be preceded by a determination of the direction and speed of the *ether wind*. Basically, the Michelson–Morley apparatus is just a differential version of the apparatus used for comparing material lengths and optical standing waves.

Numerically speaking, the importance of the preceding remarks is diminished precisely to the extent that the absolute measurements are less accurate than the relative measurements: the precision in absolute metrological comparisons is of the order of 1 part in 10^8, and a simple calculation shows that this would permit the detection of an ether wind of 50 km/sec (if it existed). But the most precise repetition of the Michelson–Morley experiment, due to Joos (Jena, 1930) would have permitted the detection of an ether wind of 1.5 km/sec.

We conclude from the preceding remarks that *it is essentially the negative result of the Michelson–Morley experiment that underlies the unconditional equivalence of the material standard and the optical standard in the measurement of lengths*. But with the advent of wave mechanics, this equivalence has become almost a truism. For wave mechanics regards a solid body as formed by a (very complicated) system of stationary matter waves, and there is clearly no reason to believe that the kinematical behavior of a standing matter wave should be different from that of a standing light wave. We have here an example of the profound kinship of special relativity and wave mechanics.

Hertzian chronometry is to classical chronometry what optical measurement of lengths is to classical measurement of lengths; the period of a Hertzian or optical wave is here taken as the standard of time. Here also wave mechanics permits an interesting remark, closely analogous to the preceding one. The material wave associated with the uniform rectilinear inertial motion of a free particle is a plane monochromatic wave. We thus see that the substitution of a Hertzian standard for a mechanical standard of time does not represent a *physical* change of the standard of time. A similar remark holds, of course, in the case of a particle acted upon by a force.

To take the length of a standing optical wave as standard of length, and with it a Hertzian or optical period as standard of time, is *ipso facto* to make *c* an absolute constant *by definition* (by definition of the standards of length and time). We have to realize clearly that this body of definitions is essentially *permitted* and *suggested* (and not imposed!) by the negative result of the Michelson–Morley experiment. This is a striking

illustration of the epistemological views of Duhem [5] and of
Poincaré, [6] according to whom, respectively (1), an experimental
fact *does not impose* but *suggests* and *permits* a hypothesis, and
(2) a hypothesis is equivalent to a set of definitions.

Conceptually speaking, the most direct method of measuring
c would consist of a double comparison: of an optical wavelength with a standard meter, and of a Hertzian or optical
period with the astronomical second. There are two modern
methods of measuring c that follow this scheme very closely:
that of the resonating Hertzian cavity, where one determines its
dimensions optically and then measures its actual resonance
frequency (Essen); and that of molecular band spectra (Plyler,
and independently, Rank *et al.*) where one measures the wavelengths of a system of spectral lines by optical means and their
periods by Hertzian means. These methods, together with others
more in the classical vein—light beams chopped at high frequency by a Kerr cell, which is a modern version of the method of the
toothed wheel (Bergstrand); radar echoes—have yielded re-
markably concordant values of c over a very large range of
wavelengths. The value of c recommended in 1964 by the
Journal of the Optical Society of America is

$$c \approx (299,792.5 \pm 0.3) \text{ km/sec.}$$

Let us finally correct a belief that has had a hardy life. People
have sometimes said that if experiment revealed secular variations in the value of c in terms of the standard meter and the
astronomical second, the whole edifice of the theory of relativity
would collapse. The preceding remarks show that this view is
completely erroneous. Such secular variations would signify one
of two things: either secular variations in the relationship of the
standard meter to wavelengths of light waves of atomic origin

---

[5] "La Théorie Physique, son Objet, sa Structure." Rivière, Paris, 1914.
[6] "La Science et l'Hypothèse." Flammarion, Paris, 1906.

(which is almost certainly excluded *a priori*,[7] since wave mechanics represents a solid body as a system of stationary matter waves): or else secular variations in the relationship of the astronomical second to Hertzian or optical periods of molecular or atomic origin, which indeed was actually the case in the days when the rotation of the earth served as the standard of astronomical time.

1.6   Conclusion

The Hertzian techniques, and those remarkable newcomers the Mössbauer effect (1958), and the stimulated emission in phase of Hertzian or visible radiation (maser effect, 1955, and laser effect, 1960), open up remarkable possibilities for variants of the Michelson–Morley experiment, the measurement of the Doppler effect, measurements of c, etc.

It is still too early to present a detailed discussion of these matters. Nevertheless, we have thought it worthwhile, even in a précis, to devote an appreciable amount of space to the discussion of the physical basis of so important a theory as special relativity.

B.   Tensors in Euclidean and Pseudo-Euclidean Spaces

1.7   Cartesian Axes in a Euclidean or Pseudo-Euclidean Space. Covariant and Contravariant Components of a Vector

Let e_i, $i = 1, 2, ..., n$ be a system of n linearly independent base

----

[7] From 1892, the date of the first measurements of Michelson and Benoit, to 1960, the date of the official adoption of a Krypton line as the standard of length, and beyond, all metrological comparisons between material standards and optical radiations are consistent among themselves to within better than one part in a million.

vectors. By linear independence we mean that it is impossible to find n numbers x^i, not all zero, such that

$$\sum x^i e_i = 0, \qquad \text{or} \qquad x^i e_i = 0, \tag{1-4}$$

where we are using the summation convention on dummy indices.[8]

Every vector A of the n-dimensional space spanned by the e_i can be expressed in the form

$$A = A^i e_i, \tag{1-5}$$

where the *contravariant components* A^i are the oblique coordinates, in the usual sense, of the tip of the vector. The covariant components of the metrical tensor are, by definition,

$$g_{ij} \equiv \tfrac{1}{2}(e_i e_j + e_j e_i). \tag{1-6}$$

They allow us to define the *covariant components* of A as follows:

$$A_i = g_{ij} A^j. \tag{1-7}$$

On the assumption that the determinant $|g_{ij}|$ is nonzero, the Cramer system of equations (7) has an inverse of the form

$$A^i = g^{ij} A_j, \tag{1-8}$$

where the g^{ij}, the *normalized minors* of the g_{ij}, are by definition the *contravariant components* of the metrical tensor. The square, A^2, of the length of A can be written in the three forms

$$A^2 = g_{ij} A^i A^j = A^i A_i = g^{ij} A_i A_j. \tag{1-9}$$

If δ^i_j denotes the Kronecker symbol ($\delta^i_j = 0$ if $i \neq j$, $= 1$ if $i = j$), the δ^i_j, by definition, represent the set of *mixed components* of the metrical tensor. Because of formulas (7), (8), and

$$A^i = \delta^i_j A^j, \qquad A_i = \delta^j_i A_j, \tag{1-10}$$

g_{ij}, g^{ij}, and δ^i_j are respectively spoken of as operators for lowering, raising, and substituting indices.

---

[8] Compare the remarks following Eq. (2).

The interpretation of the covariant components of a vector is easily found. The scalar product $A \cdot e_i$ of A with one of the base vectors can be written $A_i e^i$ with only the corresponding monomial nonzero. A_i is thus the directed distance from the origin O to the intersection of the axis along e_i with the perpendicular $(n-1)$-dimensional hyperplane passing through the extremity of A. Figure 1 shows the significance of the covariant and contravariant components of a vector in the two-dimensional case.

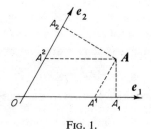

FIG. 1.

1.8 Change of Oblique Axes

The formula for this is that of a linear substitution [9]

$$x^{i'} = a^{i'}_j x^j. \qquad (1\text{-}11)$$

On the assumption that the determinant $|a^i_j|$ is nonzero, the Cramer system of equations (11) has an inverse of the form

$$x^i = a^i_{j'} x^{j'} \qquad (1\text{-}12)$$

and, by virtue of the properties of determinants, we have the double set of identities

$$a^{i'}_j a^j_{k'} = \delta^{i'}_{k'}, \qquad a^{j'}_k a^i_{j'} = \delta^i_k. \qquad (1\text{-}13)$$

---

[9] We have adopted a notation designed to simplify the typography as much as possible.

The systems of equations (11) and (12) imply

$$x_{i'} = a_{i'}^j x_j, \qquad x_i = a_i^{j'} x_{j'},   \tag{1-14}$$

and *vice versa*.

1.9   Change of Orthogonal Axes with Equal Scales of Length (Cartesian Axes in the Strict Sense)

We lose no generality if we take the common length of the base vectors to be the unit of length. In this case, denoting the Kronecker symbol by δ^{ij} or δ_{ij}, we have

$$g_{ij} = \delta_{ij}, \qquad g^{ij} = \delta^{ij},   \tag{1-15}$$

from which it follows that each covariant component of a vector is now equal to its corresponding contravariant component, and that the square of the length of a vector, defined by (9), reduces to the Pythagorean formula

$$A_i = A^i, \qquad A^2 = \sum A_i^2.   \tag{1-16}$$

The linear substitutions corresponding to changes of strictly Cartesian axes are called *linear orthogonal substitutions*. Their coefficients, which we shall denote by $O_{j'}^i$, satisfy the relations

$$\sum_{i=1}^n O_j^i O_{k'}^i = \delta_{j'k'}   \tag{1-17}$$

which, together with the general relations (13), give the characteristic formula of the orthogonal substitutions

$$O_{j'}^i = O_i^{j'}.   \tag{1-18}$$

It is clear from (17) and (18) that the squares of the two determinants $|O_{j'}^i|$ and $|O_i^{j'}|$ are equal and have the value 1; these two determinants therefore are both equal to $+1$ or both equal to -1. If their value is $+1$, we say that the two systems of axes, or ennuples, have the same sense, or that we can go from one to the other by a rotation; if their value is -1, the two ennuples are said to be of opposite sense or obtained the one from the other by a rotation combined with a reflection.

1.10 Definition of a Tensor. Rules of Tensorial Homogeneity

If a set of numbers transforms according to the law

$$T^{i'j'\cdots}{}_{k'l'\cdots} = a_i^{i'} a_j^{j'} \cdots a_{k'}^{k} a_{l'}^{l} \cdots T^{ij\cdots}{}_{kl\cdots}, \qquad (1\text{-}19)$$

we say that they represent the set of mixed components, covariant in k, l,..., and contravariant in i, j,..., of a tensor of rank equal to the number of indices. The other sets of components of the same tensor T are obtained by raising, lowering, and substitution of indices.

The homogeneity of tensor formulas, exhibited in all the preceding tensor formulas,[10] requires that, in every monomial, the dummy indices (implying summation) occur in pairs, once above and once below, and that in every sum of monomials the upper and lower identifying indices be the same (same names, and same covariant or contravariant character) in all terms of the sum.

Contraction is the operation of taking a superscript and a subscript, originally not dummy indices, and making them the same, thus giving rise to a summation.

Particular cases: a tensor of rank 0 is a *scalar* or an *invariant*; a tensor of rank 1 is a *vector*.

Symmetry and antisymmetry in two indices are characterized respectively by the relations

$$T^{ij} = T^{ji}, \qquad T^{ij} = - T^{ji} \qquad (1\text{-}20)$$

---

[10] Formulas such as (17) and (18) are, strictly speaking, not tensor formulas.

and are easily seen to be preserved when the two indices are lowered (or raised).

Decomposition of a tensor of the second rank into its symmetric and antisymmetric parts: we write

$$T^{ij} = T^{ij}_{\underline{\ }} + T^{ij}_{\vee}, \tag{1-21}$$

where
$$2T^{ij}_{\underline{\ }} = T^{ij} + T^{ji}, \qquad 2T^{ij}_{\vee} = T^{ij} - T^{ji}. \tag{1-22}$$

1.11   Components of Hypervolumes of Order $p \leqslant n$

Let x_i^j $(j=1, 2,..., n; i=1, 2,..., p)$ denote the jth contravariant component of the ith vector of a linearly independent system, and let $[x^i x^j \cdots x^k]$ denote the determinants (with their correct signs) formed from the matrix $\|x_i^j\|$ and specified by their columns. The quantities $[x^i x^j \cdots x^k]$ are the contravariant components of a completely antisymmetric tensor of rank p, and they generalize the usual concept of surface, or of volume, defined by an exterior or a mixed product.

In particular, we can consider the determinant $[e^i e^j \cdots e^k]$ of the system of axes that is being used. This is a completely antisymmetric tensor of rank n, and two systems of coordinates related by a linear substitution have the same sense or not according as the determinants of their axes have the same sign or not.

If the coordinates are not strictly Cartesian, an appropriate coefficient is needed before the tensors $[x^i x^j \cdots x^k]$ in order that they represent the true measures of generalized volumes.

Let us recall that there are four equivalent ways of forming the product of two determinants, and that the value of their product is the product of the values of the given determinants. The product
$$\omega^2 \equiv |g_{ij}| \cdot |x^i_{(a)}| \cdot |x^j_{(b)}|$$

of the three determinants shown (where, for clarity, parentheses are placed around the indices a, b numbering the x^i vectors) can thus be written in the form

$$\omega^2 = |g_{ij}x^i_{(a)}x^j_{(b)}| = |x^i_{(a)}x_{(b)i}|.$$

This shows that ω^2 is a true scalar. Denoting the value of the determinant $|g_{ij}|$ by g, as is customary, and setting $\varepsilon = \pm 1$, we see that the quantity

$$\omega = \varepsilon\sqrt{g}\,|x^i_{(a)}|$$

is a true scalar, and thus that the coefficient we sought is $\varepsilon\sqrt{g}$.

Since $g^{ij}\,g_{jk} = \delta^i_k$, we see that $|g^{ij}| = 1/g$.

1.12   Dual Tensors

A completely antisymmetric tensor of rank p possesses, apart from signs, C^p_n nonzero components. We can define another completely antisymmetric tensor, the *dual* tensor, of rank $n-p$, having the same number $C^{n-p}_n = C^p_n$ of nonzero components, such that

$$T'^{ij\cdots} = \varepsilon T^{kl\cdots}, \qquad \varepsilon = \pm 1, \tag{1-23}$$

the sequence $i, j, \ldots,\, k, l, \ldots$, containing each index once and once only and being an even permutation of the natural numbers $1, 2, 3, \ldots, n$. The sign ε must be changed if we change the sense of the ennuple.

We can give this formula its canonical tensorial form by introducing the Levi–Civita indicator $\varepsilon^{ij\cdots}$ or $\varepsilon_{ij\ldots}$ whose value, by definition, is zero if two (or more) indices are equal, and $+1$ or -1 according as the permutation of the indices (all different) is of even or odd class:

$$p!\,T'^{ij\cdots} = \varepsilon^{ij\cdots kl\cdots}T_{kl\cdots} \tag{1-24}$$

The expression $\varepsilon_{ij\ldots k}\,[x^i x^j \cdots x^k]$ is precisely the value of the determinant $|x^i_{(a)}|$ considered at the end of §11. It follows that $\varepsilon\sqrt{g}\,\varepsilon_{ij\ldots k}$ and $(\varepsilon/\sqrt{g})\,\varepsilon^{ij\ldots k}$ are respectively the covariant and contravariant components of a completely antisymmetric tensor of rank n. It is called the *gage tensor*.

The dual of a completely antisymmetric tensor of rank n is a *pseudoscalar*, that is to say a scalar that changes sign if one changes the sense of the ennuple.

In three-dimensional space, the dual of the exterior product of two "polar vectors" is an "axial vector" whose sense depends on that of the reference triad.

1.13   Differentiation in Cartesian Coordinates

The operators

$$\partial_i \equiv \frac{\partial}{\partial x^i}, \qquad \partial^i \equiv \frac{\partial}{\partial x_i} \tag{1-25}$$

are here tensor (vector) operators.[11]

The operators

$$\partial^{ij\cdots} = \partial^i \, \partial^j \cdots \tag{1-26}$$

are the components of a symmetric tensor[11] operator. We shall often have to use the *d'Alembertian operator*

$$\Box \equiv \partial_i^i. \tag{1-27}$$

1.14   General Formula for Transformation of Multiple Integrals

$$\int_{p+1} \partial^i T \, [dx_i \, dx_j \cdots dx_r] = \oint_p T \, [dx_j \cdots dx_r], \tag{1-28}$$

where the integral of order p is taken over the boundary of the

---

[11] This is, of course, not true in curvilinear coordinates, nor *a fortiori* in non-Euclidean spaces (cf. the concept of covariant derivative treated in all books on the tensor calculus).

integral of order $p+1$, and T denotes a tensor that can have indices contracted with those of the [   ].

This formula can be proved without difficulty by means of the formula for the definite integral in one variable, following the classical procedure that leads to the formulas of Stokes and Green.

Chapter 2

KINEMATICS AND OPTICS

2.1 The Symmetry of the Roles of Space and Time in Kinematics

This symmetry had escaped the notice of classical physicists because of the smallness of the velocities in ordinary mechanics compared with c. Yet it is immediately apparent in the formulas of optics—for example, in the elementary expression for the phase of a plane wave moving along the x-axis in the positive direction:

$$\varphi = \varphi_0 \cos 2\pi\left(\frac{t}{T} - \frac{x}{L}\right), \qquad L = cT, \qquad (2\text{-}1)$$

where L is the wavelength and T the period of the plane wave. In terms of wave mechanics,[1] optics is a limiting case of mechanics: that of a material point of zero rest mass, which, because of this, moves with the limiting speed c.

Because it is a limiting form of wave mechanics, optics provides a specially simple deduction of the formulas of the actual kinematics of physics. But there is nothing essential about this special simplicity, and nowadays, by taking appropriate pre-

---

[1] In this introductory paragraph we deliberately anticipate conclusions of both special relativity and wave mechanics: we wish to immerse the reader right from the start in the atmosphere of the classical theories of the twentieth century.

cautions of language (notably concerning phase and group velocities), all the arguments that we shall present in this chapter on the basis of optics could be repeated, with minimal changes of wording, in terms of wave mechanics.

A. Einstein–Minkowski Kinematics

2.2 Relativistic Equivalence of Space and Time

In a region of empty space traversed by light waves, consider two points P_1 and P_2 separated by a finite interval having co-ordinate differences Δx^u $(u = 1, 2, 3)$. Astronomical observation of the occultations of stars by distant planets, such as Jupiter, has shown that there is no measurable dispersion in the vacuum and thus that the value of the speed c of light waves, to a very high degree of accuracy, is independent of the frequency. More-over, the Michelson–Morley experiment has shown (§1.2) that the value of c, measured with a material standard of length and a standard of time that is the period of the radiation employed, is independent of every type of what we may call "speed of ether drag" of the reference frame. If, then, Δt is the time taken by the light to travel from P_1 to P_2 (we can imagine a source at P_1 and a receiver at P_2) we have from the definition of c the relation

$$\Delta x_u \, \Delta x^u - c^2 \, \Delta t^2 = 0. \qquad (2\text{-}2)$$

The Michelson–Morley experiment shows that we have the right to consider c an absolute constant (constant by the very defi-nitions of the standards of length and time).

The discussion of the *principle of relativity* (§§1.1 and 1.2) showed us that it is important to specify the space frame that is used. In conformity with the idea of Mascart, Poincaré, Lorentz, and Einstein that the *principle of relativity of dynamics* is the prototype of the *universal physical principle of relativity* (called nowadays the *special principle of relativity*), we shall assume that *the three spatial intervals Δx^u are evaluated in a Galilean frame.*

The fundamental difference between classical and relativistic kinematics (as we shall see in a moment) is that *the time interval Δt can no longer be considered absolute, as Newton and his followers had believed; it too is relative to the frame of reference.*

This leads us to introduce the concept of a *Galilean spatio-temporal reference frame*, x^1, x^2, x^3, t, also called (to emphasize the transition from the old kinematics to the new) a *Lorentzian reference frame in space-time.*

The *universal special principle of relativity* can be given mathematical form by expressing the privileged equivalence of the Lorentzian frames, that is by writing the formulas of the group of transformations that leave the expression (2) invariant.

As Minkowski pointed out, if we write

$$x^4 = ict, \qquad i = \sqrt{-1}, \tag{2-3}$$

the expression (2) can be written in the condensed symmetric form

$$\Delta x_i \, \Delta x^i = 0, \tag{2-4}$$

where

$$x^i = x^1, \quad x^2, \quad x^3, \quad ict. \tag{2-5}$$

Geometrically, the natural idea is to imagine, with Minkowski, that we have completed the Galilean trihedral $Ox^1x^2x^3$ by adding to it a fourth axis, orthogonal to the first three, on which we place the variable i*ct*. Formula (2) or (4) then says that *the law of propagation of light is such that the square of the space-time interval Δx^1, Δx^2, Δx^3, ic Δt is zero*; according to *the special principle of relativity*, the law must remain *identically true in all Lorentzian systems of space-time coordinates*; and this is so for all finite Δx^i satisfying (4).

If we postulate that the formulas for the change of variables shall be linear, i.e., of the form (1-11), a simple calculation shows that the invariance of the left hand side of (4) implies the relation (1-17), which expresses the *orthogonality* of the linear substitution. Thus *the Lorentzian space-time frames are none other than the strictly Cartesian frames* (axes orthogonal and having equal scales). The law of the privileged equivalence of the Lorentzian frames (the special principle of relativity) immediately receives an extremely simple geometrical interpretation: *it is identical to the privileged equivalence of the strictly Cartesian coordinates in a Euclidean space* [here *pseudo-Euclidean*, to take account of the minus sign in (2) or the presence of i in $(4)^2$].

Let A be any space-time vector with components X^1, X^2, X^3, $X^4 = icT$. The square of its length

$$A^2 \equiv X_i X^i = X_u X^u - c^2 T^2 \tag{2-6}$$

can be positive, negative, or zero. If $A^2 > 0$, then $X_u X^u > c^2 T^2$, and A is said to be *spacelike*; if $A^2 < 0$, then $X_u X^u < c^2 T^2$, and A is said to be *timelike*; and if $A^2 = 0$, then $X_u X^u = c^2 T^2$, and A is said to be *isotropic* or *null* (and it is in terms of this last case that we have been reasoning).

The equation

$$x_i x^i = 0 \tag{2-7}$$

is that of the *null cone* with vertex at O. Its exterior contains the ends of the *spacelike* vectors issuing from O, and this region is usually called *elsewhere*. The interior of the cone contains the ends of the timelike vectors. As we see, it contains two regions, and these are usually called *future* and *past*. All of this will be fully justified in the course of §3.

We shall now develop the consequences of these principles (that is, of the *special theory of relativity*) using the purely

---

[2] We have deliberately excluded the hypothesis

$$\Delta x_{i'} \Delta x^{i'} = f(\beta) \Delta x_i \Delta x^i$$

which would be contrary to the principle that all Lorentz frames are equivalent.

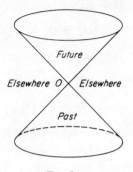

FIG. 2.

imaginary coordinate $x^4 = ict$ throughout. The obvious advantage in so doing is that we work with strictly Cartesian coordinates, and there is no need to distinguish between covariant and contra-variant components of tensors (though we shall do so neverthe-less in order to preserve the usual tensorial forms of equations).

2.3 "The Second Law" of the Theory of Relativity

The discovery by Joule of an *equivalence* (expressed by a linear formula) between the entities *work* and *heat* enhanced the need for the formulation of the *second law*, stressing the *differences* between work and heat. Analogously, Einstein's discovery of an *equivalence* (expressed by a quadratic formula) between *space* and *time* creates an urgent need to formulate a *second principle* clearly expressing the differences between space and time.

The various aspects of the *second principle of the theory of relativity* all result from the variables 1, 2, 3 being real and the variable 4 being pure imaginary.

To start with, the coefficients $O_i^{j'}$ of the coordinate transfor-mation (formulas (1-11)) will be real if they contain the index 4 either twice or not at all, and pure imaginary if they contain it once. From (1-13) we obtain, in particular

$$(O_4^4)^2 = 1 - O_4^{u'} O_{u'}^4 \qquad (O_4^{4'} = O_{4'}^4 = O_4^4, \quad O_4^{u'} = O_{u'}^4), \qquad (2\text{-}8)$$

and therefore, since the sum $O_4^{u'} O_{u'}^4$ is intrinsically negative,

$$(O_4^4)^2 \geqslant 1, \qquad (2\text{-}9)$$

so that

$$O_4^4 \leqslant -1 \qquad \text{or} \qquad O_4^4 \geqslant +1. \qquad (2\text{-}10)$$

These are statements in the form of inequalities characteristic of a *second law*.

Let us now postulate that the formulas for changing physical Lorentz frames form a continuous group. Then the first of the inequalities in (10) is excluded, since it implies a reversal of the direction of the time axis, and there remains

$$\boxed{O_4^4 \geqslant +1} \qquad (2\text{-}11)$$

If, in particular, $O_4^4 = +1$, the Lorentz transformation reduces to

$$t' = t, \qquad x^{u'} = O_v^{u'} x^v, \qquad (2\text{-}12)$$

the nine $O_v^{u'}$ therefore being the coefficients of a rotation of the spatial axes.

To study a change of Lorentz frames involving relative motion, let us take $O_4^4 > +1$. To "follow the motion" of the origin O of the spatial axes x^u, we set $x^u = 0$, whence

$$x^{u'} = O_4^{u'} x^4, \qquad x^{4'} = O_4^{4'} x^4, \qquad (2\text{-}13)$$

and consequently

$$x^{u'} = \frac{1}{O_4^4} O_4^{u'} x^{4'} = \frac{ic}{O_4^4} O_4^{u'} t'. \qquad (2\text{-}14)$$

The three real quantities $icO_4^{u'}/O_4^4$ represent the components v^u of the velocity of the spatial origin of the unprimed frame in the primed frame. In relativity it is customary to write

$$\beta^u \equiv \frac{1}{c} v^u. \qquad (2\text{-}15)$$

Using this notation, we have, finally,

$$v^{u'} = \frac{ic}{O_4^4} O_4^{u'}, \qquad \beta^{u'} = \frac{i}{O_4^4} O_4^{u'}. \qquad (2\text{-}16)$$

The three components $\beta^{u'}$ can thus be interpreted as three direction coefficients of the Ox^4 axis in the quadruple $Ox^{i'}$.

Forming the scalar product $\beta^{u'}\beta_{u'} = \beta'^2$ and taking account of (1-17) and (1-18), we obtain

$$\beta^2 = \frac{(O_4^4)^2 - 1}{(O_4^4)^2}, \qquad O_4^4 = \frac{1}{\sqrt{1 - \beta^2}}. \qquad (2\text{-}17)$$

From this and the second formula of (16) we conclude first that $\beta^2 = \beta'^2$: the velocity of the spatial origin of the frame x in the frame x' has a magnitude equal to that of the velocity of the spatial origin of the frame x' in the frame x. And then, since O_4^4 is real, we conclude that

$$\beta^2 \leqslant 1, \qquad v^2 \leqslant c^2: \qquad (2\text{-}18)$$

the relative velocity of the spatial origins of the two physical Lorentz frames necessarily has magnitude less than c.

From this we easily conclude that the time axes of the physical Lorentz frames are all timelike (and their spatial axes therefore spacelike); and that *the sign of the fourth component of a timelike vector is the same in all physical Lorentz frames.*

2.4 Particles and Point Observers

Consider a particle whose spatial coordinates x^u are functions of the time t, the x^u and t belonging to the same Lorentz frame. Experiment shows that there always exists a physical Lorentz frame in which the point is at rest. It follows from this that the *spatio-temporal trajectory* of the particle x^i ($i = 1, 2, 3, 4$) is everywhere timelike and that at each of its points (point-instants) we can define a *tangent Lorentz frame*,[3] i.e., a Lorentz frame whose time axis is tangent to the trajectory at the origin. As a corollary, *the physical speed of a particle is always less than c.*

Making a somewhat radical idealization, the theory of relativity introduces the concept of the *point observer* whose body is reduced to a particle. It then assumes as a *principle* that the time lived by such an observer is obtained by integration of the tangent Lorentz times, i.e., that it is measured by the curvilinear element $ds = ic\, d\tau$ $(ds^2 = dx^i\, dx_i;\ d\tau$ *proper time*). The theory postulates further that the observational space of such an observer, at each of its point-instants, is the three-dimensional flat manifold normal to the curve.

All of relativistic physics will be expressible in terms of geometry and the four-dimensional tensor calculus. The homogeneity of the formulas will evidently require that the components of a tensor be real or pure imaginary according as they contain the index 4 an even or odd number of times.

B. Einstein–Minkowski Kinematics (Continuation)

2.5 The Special Lorentz Transformation

In making a change of Lorentz reference frame we can take the two axes $x^1 = x$ and $x^{1'} = x'$ (for example) in the plane of the two axes $x^4 = ict$ and $x^{4'} = ict'$. The "kinematic" part of the transformation (13) then reduces to

$$x' = \frac{x + vt}{\sqrt{1 - \beta^2}}, \qquad x = \frac{x' - vt'}{\sqrt{1 - \beta^2}},$$

$$t' = \frac{t + c^{-2}vx}{\sqrt{1 - \beta^2}}; \qquad t = \frac{t' - c^{-2}vx'}{\sqrt{1 - \beta^2}}; \qquad (2\text{-}19)$$

---

[3] Modulo an unimportant rotation of the spatial axes.

the two other pairs of formulas having to do merely with a rotation of the spatial axes $x^2 = y$ and $x^3 = z$; and we lose no generality by simply taking

$$y' = y, \qquad z' = z. \tag{2-20}$$

Let us recall that the kinematic transformation formulas of Galileo and Newton were

$$x' = x + vt, \qquad t' = t. \tag{2-21}$$

They can be obtained from (19) by neglecting the terms in c^{-2}. We can summarize the situation by saying that in the usual amalgamation of space and time the *elsewhere* region of the isotropic cone appears quite flat, and that the approximation corresponding to classical kinematics consists in removing the *elsewhere* region from the space-time diagram (Figs. 2 and 3).

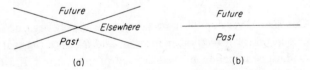

FIG. 3. (a) Relativistic kinematics. (b) Classical kinematics.

If we use space-time variables that are all real, namely x, y, z, and

$$u = ct \tag{2-22}$$

and write

$$\beta = \tanh \varphi \tag{2-23}$$

we can write (19) in the form

$$\begin{cases} x' = x \cosh \varphi + u \sinh \varphi, \\ u' = x \sinh \varphi + u \cosh \varphi, \end{cases}$$
$$\begin{cases} x = x' \cosh \varphi - u' \sinh \varphi, \\ u = -x' \sinh \varphi + u' \cosh \varphi. \end{cases} \tag{2-24}$$

These are the formulas of the "hyperbolic rotation" illustrated in Fig. 4.

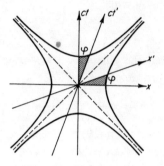

FIG. 4.

2.6   Slowing of Clocks and Lorentz Contraction

Consider a very small material system, ideally regarded as a point, in uniform rectilinear motion, and let it be the seat of a periodic phenomenon of well-defined proper period T_0 (in the sense of the end of §4). In every Lorentz frame in which the system is not at rest, the fourth component icT of the proper vector of length icT_0 is such that

$$T = \frac{T_0}{\sqrt{1 - \beta^2}} > T_0. \qquad (2\text{-}25)$$

This is the phenomenon of the *dilatation of periods* by motion, a phenomenon that is *relative* to the Lorentz frame used.

This phenomenon, moreover, is *reciprocal* in the sense that if two "clocks" conforming to the preceding definition and having the same proper period T_0 are both in inertial motion with relative speed $v = \beta c$, the relative evaluation of either of the two periods in the reference frame of the other clock yields the same ratio:

$$\frac{T_2}{(T_0)_1} = \frac{T_1}{(T_0)_2} = \frac{1}{\sqrt{1 - \beta^2}}.$$

This phenomenon, which seemed most surprising in the early days of the theory of relativity, is almost self-evident from the point of view of four-dimensional geometry (see Fig. 5a).

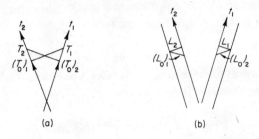

(a)   (b)

FIG. 5. (a) Dilatation of periods by motion. (b) Contraction of lengths by motion.

Again, given a material measuring rod of proper length L_0, let us consider the natural evaluation L of its length in a Lorentz frame with respect to which it is moving with speed v "parallel to its length." L is merely the spatial interval separating the intersections of the space-time trajectories of the ends of the rod with a hyperplane $t = $ const of the nonproper frame. We obviously have (see Fig. 5b)

$$L = L_0 \sqrt{1 - \beta^2} < L_0. \qquad (2\text{-}26)$$

This is the phenomenon of the Lorentz–Fitzgerald *longitudinal contraction of lengths*, a phenomenon that is *relative* to the Lorentz frame that is used.

Like the previous one, this phenomenon is *reciprocal*, in the sense that if, in ordinary space, two material measuring rods of equal proper length L_0 slide one upon the other with relative speed $v = \beta c$, the evaluation of the length of each in the proper

Lorentz frame of the other is such that

$$\frac{L_2}{(L_0)_1} = \frac{L_1}{(L_0)_2} = \sqrt{1 - \beta^2}.$$

This is no more preposterous than the fact that in both the theory and observation of classical perspective each of two observers actually of equal height finds that the other, seen from afar, is smaller than his lifesize model nearby.

2.7 Law of Composition of Parallel Velocities. Application to the Fresnel–Fizeau Formula

Let 1, 2, 3 be three Lorentz trihedrals such that the relative speeds $v_{2,1}$ and $v_{3,2}$ are parallel in the usual observational sense. We seek the value of the velocity $v_{3,1}$, which is manifestly parallel to the preceding velocities.

The problem is that of the composition of hyperbolic tangents. We have

$$\tanh \theta_{3,1} = \tanh(\theta_{2,1} + \theta_{3,2}) = \frac{\tanh \theta_{2,1} + \tanh \theta_{3,2}}{1 + \tanh \theta_{2,1} \tanh \theta_{3,2}},$$

(2-27)

which at once gives

$$v_{3,1} = \frac{v_{2,1} + v_{3,2}}{1 + \beta_{2,1}\beta_{3,2}}$$
$$= (v_{2,1} + v_{3,2})(1 - \beta_{2,1}\beta_{3,2} + \cdots).$$ (2-28)

This is the *relativistic law of composition of velocities*, which differs from the additive classical law by a correction in c^{-2}.

Von Laue pointed out that the Fresnel–Fizeau ether-drag formula is a direct consequence of the law of composition (28). For let c/n be the speed of light in a medium of refractive index n. Then if the medium is made to move with speed v in a particular Lorentz frame, the speed, c', of the waves measured parallel to

v would have the value

$$c' = \frac{c/n \pm v}{1 \pm v/nc} = \left(\frac{c}{n} \pm v\right)\left(1 \mp \frac{v}{nc} + \cdots\right),$$

and on neglecting terms of higher order than the first in v we obtain precisely (1-3).

2.8   Converse: Relativistic Kinematics Deduced from the First Order Effect and the Postulate of a Group Structure[4]

Let us postulate the Fresnel drag law (1-3), and write it in terms of a time unit ct

$$w = u + v(1 - u^2). \qquad (2\text{-}29)$$

Since v is small compared with u, w, and $1 - u$, let us postulate that we are dealing with the infinitesimal form of a law of composition of velocities.

More precisely, let us postulate that we are dealing with the generating formula of a continuous, connected group and that the set of velocities is ordered. It follows from the theory of one-parameter groups that the group we seek is isomorphic with the additive group of the real numbers, i.e., that the law of composition will have the form

(a) $$F(w) = F(u) + F(v)$$

where, since $w = u$ for $v = 0$,

(b) $$F(0) = 0.$$

By virtue of the initial postulate, (29) is the start of a Taylor series in powers of v, and we thus have

(c) $$1 - u^2 = \frac{\partial}{\partial v} w(u, 0) = \left\{\frac{F'(v)}{F'(w)}\right\}_{v=0} = \frac{F'(0)}{F'(u)}$$

[4] Abelé and Malvaux, "Vitesse et Univers Relativiste." S.E.D.E.S., Paris, 1954.

so that

(d) $F'(u) = \dfrac{A}{1 - u^2},$ $F(u) = \dfrac{A}{2} \log \dfrac{1 + u}{1 - u},$

where A is a constant. Using this result in (a) we find

(e) $\dfrac{1 + w}{1 - w} = \dfrac{1 + u}{1 - u} \cdot \dfrac{1 + v}{1 - v},$ $w = \dfrac{u + v}{1 + uv},$

which is the relativistic law of composition of velocities (28).

We leave it to the reader to go back from (28) to (24) on the assumption that the velocities u, v, w are the relative velocities of three Lorentz frames.

Abelé and Malvaux call the expression $v = (u - w)/(1 - uw)$ the kinematic difference between two velocities u and w, this being expressible in the infinitesimal form[5]

$$Dv = \frac{dv}{1 - u^2}. \tag{2-30}$$

It is worth noting too, as they pointed out, that the relativistic law of composition of velocities (e) has an anharmonic form.

These considerations of Abelé and Malvaux point up the hybrid character of the simple adjunction of the Fresnel drag law to classical kinematics. When we postulate a group structure, the equivalence of classical and relativistic kinematics to the first order is seen to be fallacious, relativistic kinematics being the only one that is intrinsically self-consistent.

2.9   "Absolute" Character of Rotations in Optics. The Harress–Sagnac Effect

This has to do with a sort of optical analog of the Foucault

---

[5] An application of this concept is given at the end of §4.5.

pendulum experiment. The effect is of the first order in β, and the theory, which is experimentally verified, can be worked out equally well either in terms of classical kinematics (plus the Fresnel–Fizeau formula in the Harress case) or of relativistic kinematics.

The experiment consists in causing two beams of monochromatic light (obtained by separation of a single initial beam) to interfere after having made them travel in opposite directions around the same circuit, the material elements of this circuit being carried around by a rotating disk. This polygonal circuit is shaped by means of plane mirrors. In the experiment of Harress (1912) the light traveled within glass prisms (Fig. 6a), and in that of Sagnac (1913), in air (Fig. 6b). In both cases the result was that the rotation of the disk with angular velocity ω introduced an optical retardation

$$\Delta t = 4c^{-2}\omega\mathscr{A} \qquad (2\text{-}31)$$

where $\mathscr{A}$ denotes the area of the circuit.

The exact relativistic theory of this effect requires curvilinear coordinates appropriate to the problem, and also the consideration of non-Lorentzian space-time frames. We shall content ourselves here with an argument which, though it leaves something to be desired in the way of rigor, has the advantage of being simple and intuitive (and, naturally, of leading to the correct result).

Let us take any Lorentzian reference frame $\mathscr{R}$ and neglect the component of its velocity normal to the plane of the disk. To the first order, everything is as if, at each instant t of $\mathscr{R}$, the disk turned as a whole with angular velocity ω about an "instantaneous center of rotation" I. Let $\boldsymbol{u}(P,t)$ be the unit vector tangent to the light circuit $\mathscr{L}$ at each of its points P. The component along $\boldsymbol{u}$ of the velocity of the point P has the value

$$v = (\boldsymbol{\omega} \times \boldsymbol{r}) \cdot \boldsymbol{u} = \boldsymbol{\omega} \cdot (\boldsymbol{r} \times \boldsymbol{u})$$

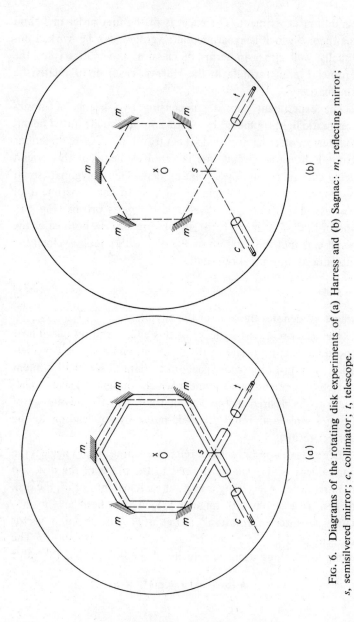

FIG. 6.   Diagrams of the rotating disk experiments of (a) Harress and (b) Sagnac: *m*, reflecting mirror; *s*, semisilvered mirror; *c*, collimator; *t*, telescope.

With respect to $\mathscr{R}$, the components along $\boldsymbol{u}$ of the speed of the light will be given by Fresnel's formula. On subtracting v, we obtain the arithmetical difference (and not the kinematic difference!) between the velocities of the light and the disk evaluated in $\mathscr{R}$:

$$c' - v = \frac{c}{n}\left(1 - \frac{\beta}{n}\right), \qquad c'' - v = \frac{c}{n}\left(1 + \frac{\beta}{n}\right),$$

and from this we obtain the following values for the times taken to travel a circuit element dl (evaluated in $\mathscr{R}$):

$$dt' = \frac{n\,dl}{c}\left(1 + \frac{\beta}{n} + \cdots\right), \qquad dt'' = \frac{n\,dl}{c}\left(1 - \frac{\beta}{n} + \cdots\right).$$

Taking the difference $\delta t = dt' - dt''$, we see that the refractive index n cancels out to the first order, so that

$$\delta t = 2c^{-2}v\,dl = 2c^{-2}\omega(\boldsymbol{r} \times \boldsymbol{dl}) = 4c^{-2}\omega\,d\mathscr{A}$$

and from this, by integration, we obtain formula (2-31).

Of course, although $c' \neq c''$ and $dt' \neq dt''$, we must not conclude that there exists a *local* optical anisotropy on the disk. We are dealing solely with an apparent anisotropy introduced by the method of calculation, and one that is proportional to the distance r between the point in question, P, and the instantaneous center I.

REMARK. *Non-Euclidean character of the geometry experienced by the inhabitants of the disk (Ehrenfest).* Let us now take I at the mechanical axis of rotation of the disk, and let R_0 be the corresponding local Lorentz frame. An inhabitant of this disk-planet situated at a point P who measures an element ds of a circle of latitude at a given instant of his proper time will obtain $1/\sqrt{1-\beta^2}$ times the value obtained by the Lorentzian observer R_0 operating at a given instant of his own proper time. However, the two observers P and R_0 will agree about the value of an element measured along a line of longitude. And since, for R_0, the ratio of the radius r_0 to the circumference l_0 of a circle of latitude has the Euclidean value

$$l_0 = 2\pi r_0,$$

the relations

$$dl = \frac{dl_0}{\sqrt{1 - \beta^2}}, \qquad dr = dr_0, \qquad \beta = \omega \frac{r}{c}$$

show that

$$l = 2\pi r/(1 - c^{-2}\omega^2 r^2)^{\frac{1}{2}}. \qquad (2\text{-}32)$$

Thus the spatial geometry of the inhabitants of the disk-planet is non-Euclidean.

Nothing catastrophic results so long as we conceive of the disk rotating with angular velocity ω as something intangible. But what happens when the disk is initially at rest, and thus has a geometry that is certainly Euclidean, and we then force it to move with increasing angular velocity? Viewed from R_0, each element along a circle of latitude will suffer the Lorentz contraction—and, incidentally, the linear velocity of every point of the disk, evaluated in R_0, must remain less than c. It appears, then, that *the problem of the rotating disk is not a purely kinematical one but that questions of elasticity and dynamics are also involved.*[6]

2.10   Spatio-Temporal Four-Frequency

Consider the classical expression (1) for the optical phase. Clearly, it can only be a space-time scalar. The expression in

[6] The relativistic problem of the rotating disk has given rise to an abundant literature starting with P. Ehrenfest, *Z. Physik* **10**, 918 (1909). It played a crucial role in the creation of the general theory of relativity by Einstein. We cannot say that it has even yet received a satisfactory solution (see, for example, G. L. Clark, *Proc. Roy. Soc. Edinburgh, Sect. A* **62**, 434 (1947), and *Proc. Cambridge Phil. Soc.* **45**, 465 (1949); also S. Kichenassamy, *Bol. Univ. Paraña* **1**, 1 (1961)).

parentheses is therefore seen to be the product of two four-vectors, $\quad x^i \quad$ and $\quad k^i(2\pi/L, 0, 0, 2\pi i/cT)$

or, for an arbitrary choice of spatial trihedral,

$$k^u = \frac{2\pi}{L}\alpha^u, \qquad \alpha^u\alpha_u = 1 ; \qquad k^4 = \frac{2\pi i}{cT}. \qquad (2\text{-}33)$$

The three α^u are the direction cosines of the direction of propagation. In the optical case, the *four-frequency* k^i is isotropic because of the relation $L = cT$. The condensed expression for the phase is thus

$$\varphi = \varphi_0 \cos k^i x_i. \qquad (2\text{-}34)$$

2.11 Doppler Effect. Aberration. Transverse Doppler Effect

The general formulas for these effects can be obtained by applying the laws of transformation (1-11), (2-19), or (2-24) to the four-frequency k^i. We confine ourselves here to particular cases.

Longitudinal Doppler effect

$$v' = v\left(\frac{1+\beta}{1-\beta}\right)^{\frac{1}{2}} = v(1 + \beta + \cdots). \qquad (2\text{-}35)$$

Aberration in the transverse case

$$\tan \alpha = \frac{k^{1'}}{2\pi c v'} = \frac{v}{c}. \qquad (2\text{-}36)$$

Transverse Doppler effect

$$v' = \frac{v}{\sqrt{1 - \beta^2}}. \qquad (2\text{-}37)$$

Equations (35) (to the first order) and (36) are the classical formulas for the Doppler and Bradley effects. Equation (37) is the formula for the purely relativistic *transverse Doppler effect*, often called the *second order Doppler effect*. The existence of this effect has been confirmed in the laboratory (Ives and Stilwell, 1941).

2.12   The Space-Time Four-Velocity

Let $v^u = dx^u/dt$ $(u = 1, 2, 3)$ be the three components of the ordinary velocity of a particle, and let us write

$$\alpha = \frac{1}{\sqrt{1 - \beta^2}}, \qquad \text{or} \qquad \alpha = \frac{dt}{d\tau}. \qquad (2\text{-}38)$$

This quantity is the cosine of the (pure imaginary) angle between the tangent to the space-time trajectory and the time axis (in the notation $x^4 = ict$; $d\tau$, of course, denotes the element of proper time). The *space-time four-velocity* is defined by

$$V^u = \alpha v^u, \qquad V^4 = ic\alpha. \qquad (2\text{-}39)$$

It is thus of unit length in c-units,

$$V_i V^i = -c^2, \qquad (2\text{-}40)$$

and can be written in the alternative form

$$V^i = \frac{dx^i}{d\tau}. \qquad (2\text{-}41)$$

2.13   Change of Lorentz Frame. Ordinary and Coriolis Inertial Effects

An infinitesimal rotation of the Lorentz quadruple can evidently be written

$$dx^i = -d\omega^{ij} x_j, \qquad (2\text{-}42)$$

where the $d\omega^{ij}$ are the components of an infinitesimal anti-symmetric tensor of the second rank. This is, in fact, the necessary and sufficient condition that the equation

$$x_i \, dx^i = 0 \tag{2-43}$$

be satisfied identically, which is the very definition of the effect of a rotation of the quadruple.

Suppose, now, that the reference quadruple is the moving quadruple associated with a small material reference body (or, if one prefers, with an "observer"): its x^4-axis, by hypothesis, is tangent to the timelike trajectory of a suitably defined mean point of the reference body, and its other axes, $x^u (u, v, w = 1, 2, 3)$, are orthogonal to the trajectory. With τ denoting the proper time of the mean point, we write

$$\Omega^{ij} = \frac{d\omega^{ij}}{d\tau}, \tag{2-44}$$

this being the instantaneous velocity of rotation of the quadruple.

As for the observed phenomena, we shall assume that we are dealing with the inertial, rectilinear, uniform motion of a real or virtual swarm of particles moving with a common four-velocity V^i; for example, particles represented by a plane monochromatic wave in wave mechanics.[7]

The acceleration $V'^i = dV^i/d\tau$ communicated to the particles of the swarm by the instantaneous change of the Lorentz reference frame will be, by (42),

$$V'^i = -\Omega^{ij}V_j. \tag{2-45}$$

If the ordinary velocities v^u are small, so that it suffices to retain only terms no higher than those of the first order in v and v', (45) can be written
$$v'^u = -\Omega^{uv}v_v - ic\Omega^{u4}, \tag{2-46}$$

[7] On this subject see, for example, Part C of Chapter 5.

or

$$v' = - \boldsymbol{\Omega} \times v - \boldsymbol{\Gamma}, \qquad (2\text{-}47)$$

where, of course, the vectors $\boldsymbol{\Omega}$ and $\boldsymbol{\Gamma}$ are thought of as

$$\Omega^{\omega} = \Omega^{uv}, \qquad \Gamma^{u} = ic\Omega^{u4}. \qquad (2\text{-}48)$$

The first term of (47) represents the Coriolis acceleration and the second the ordinary inertial acceleration. Ω^{u} and Γ^{u}, the ordinary angular velocity and acceleration of the three-dimensional reference frame, are the 6 components of a single *space-time rotation of the quadruple*.

These formulas have a purely *local* validity. They apply rigorously only to a very small element of three-dimensional reference frame that is undergoing kinematical rotation.

Although the special theory of relativity, when cleverly used, allows us to draw a certain number of plausible physical conclusions in problems involving acceleration of the reference body, the rigorous theory in these cases is always based on the general theory of relativity.

C. More Sophisticated Questions

2.14 Composition of Noncollinear Velocities [8]

In Minkowskian coordinates with $x^4 = ict$, the problem of the composition of noncollinear velocities is equivalent to that of spherical trigonometry on a sphere of radius i (Fig. 7). If $\theta_1, \theta_2, \theta_3$ and A_1, A_2, A_3 denote the sides and angles of a spherical triangle, we have the well-known formulas

$$\cos A_1 = - \cos A_2 \cos A_3 + \sin A_2 \sin A_3 \cos \theta_1$$
$$\cos \theta_1 = \cos \theta_2 \cos \theta_3 + \sin \theta_2 \sin \theta_3 \cos A_1 \qquad (2\text{-}49)$$
$$\sin \theta_2 \sin A_3 = \sin \theta_3 \sin A_2$$

---

[8] After R. Becker, *Perspectives X*, p. 74 (1961).

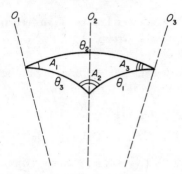

Fig. 7. Spherical triangle.

The sum of the interior angles of the triangle, which would be greater than π on a real sphere, is here less than π. As a result, three observers O_1, O_2, O_3, moving away from one another with constant relative velocities characterized by θ_1, θ_2, θ_3, and able to communicate to each other the values of the angles A_1, A_2, A_3, would be in a position to calculate not only the ratios of their velocities of flight (as in classical kinematics) but the actual values. If $2\varepsilon = \pi - A_1 - A_2 - A_3$ denotes the "spherical defect," they would use for this purpose the Borda formulas

$$i \tan \theta_1 = \left(\frac{\sin \varepsilon \sin (A_1 + \varepsilon)}{\sin (A_2 + \varepsilon) \sin (A_3 + \varepsilon)} \right)^{\frac{1}{2}} \qquad (2\text{-}50)$$

and cyclic permutations.

It is easy to return to real Minkowski coordinates with $x^4 = ct$ by the formulas

$$\cosh u = \cos \theta, \qquad \sinh u = i \sin \theta, \qquad \tanh u = i \tan \theta, \qquad (2\text{-}51)$$

and we write formulas (49) in the form

$$\cos A_1 = - \cos A_2 \cos A_3 + \sin A_2 \sin A_3 \cosh u_1$$
$$\cosh u_1 = \cosh u_2 \cosh u_3 - \sinh u_2 \sinh u_3 \cos A_1$$
$$\sinh u_2 \sin A_3 = \sinh u_3 \sin A_2 \qquad (2\text{-}52)$$

**2.15   Special Noncollinear Lorentz Transformations. [9]
Do They Form a Group? [10]**

The reader is invited, as an exercise, to put the Lorentz formulas (19) and (20) into the intrinsic form

$$O'P' = OP - v^{-1}(\alpha - 1)(OP \cdot v)v + \alpha t v,$$
$$t' = \alpha(t + c^{-2}OP \cdot v), \tag{2-53}$$

where, as usual, $\alpha = 1/(1 - \beta^2)^{\frac{1}{2}}$; then to project the vector $O'P'$ onto the axes of a trihedral $O'x'y'z'$ and the vectors OP and v onto the axes of a trihedral $Oxyz$, and to verify that the formulas thus obtained are of the form (1-11)–(1-18) with

$$O_v^u = O_u^v = (\alpha - 1)v^u v^v, \qquad (u \neq v),$$
$$O_u^u = \alpha(v^u)^2 + (v^v)^2 + (v^v)^2, \tag{2-54}$$
$$O_4^u = \mathrm{i} c^{-1}\alpha v^2 v^u, \qquad O_u^4 = -\mathrm{i} c^{-1}\alpha v^2 v^u, \qquad O_4^4 = \alpha v^2.$$

Because of (1-18), we see that the inverse transformation is obtained by changing v into $-v$.

In general, none of the axes x' coincides with one of the axes[11] x, and the preceding transformation is the most general Lorentz transformation.

Taking the derivative of (53) and writing $w = dOP/dt$ and

[9] After A. Lichnerowicz, "Eléments de Calcul Tensoriel," pp. 171–173. Armand Colin, Paris, 1950. See also G. Casanova, "Relativité Restreinte," pp. 23 and 31. Belin, Paris, 1969.

An excellent geometrical study is given by A. D. Fokker, "Time and Space, Weight and Inertia," pp. 48–76. Pergamon Press, Oxford, 1965.

[10] After V. Lalan, *Compt. Rend.* **236**, 2297 (1953); and R. Garnier, *ibid.* 2299. These articles give geometrical interpretations of the phenomenon.

[11] One must not confuse the axes of S' with the three lines which, coinciding with the axes of S at time $t = 0$, move with respect to S with a uniform rectilinear translation of velocity v. These three lines certainly remain parallel to the axes of S, but they are not the axes of S' since for them it is t and not t' that is constant (Lalan[10]).

$w' = dO'P'/dt'$, and also $\beta_0 = v/c$, $\beta = w/c$, and $\beta' = w'/c$, we find that

$$w' = \frac{\alpha^{-1}[w - v^{-2}(v \cdot w)v] + (1 + v^{-2}v \cdot w)v}{1 + \beta_0 \beta} \quad (2\text{-}55)$$

The vector within the brackets is orthogonal to v.

The reader will be able to verify that in a "cycle" of special Lorentz transformations characterized by noncollinear relative velocities v_{21}, v_{32}, v_{13} (such that, as a result, $v_{31} = -v_{13}$ is the "composed" velocity of v_{21} and v_{32}), the axes of the spatial trihedral do not return to their initial orientations at the end of the cycle. In this sense we may say that the special (noncollinear) Lorentz transformations do not form a group (although, of course, the general Lorentz transformations do form a group).

2.16 General Aberration Formula. Relativistic Photography[12]

For an isotropic four-vector, the Lorentz formulas may be written

$$x' = x \cosh u + (x^2 + y^2 + z^2)^{\frac{1}{2}} \sinh u, \qquad y' = y, \qquad z' = z. \quad (2\text{-}56)$$

From this, writing

$$\tan \alpha = \frac{(y^2 + z^2)^{\frac{1}{2}}}{x}, \qquad \tan \alpha' = \frac{(y'^2 + z'^2)^{\frac{1}{2}}}{x'}, \quad (2\text{-}57)$$

we obtain

$$\frac{1}{\tan \alpha'} = \frac{1}{\tan \alpha} \cosh u + \frac{1}{\sin \alpha} \sinh u. \quad (2\text{-}58)$$

This is the general aberration formula (Bradley effect). Becker[12]

[12] R. Penrose, *Proc. Cambridge Phil. Soc.* **55,** 137 (1959); J. Terrell, *Phys. Rev.* **116,** 1041 (1959); M. L. Boas, *Am. J. Phys.* **29,** 253 (1961). We here follow the treatment of Becker,[8] pp. 110–112.

pointed out that it takes a very simple form if we express $\sin \alpha$ and $\tan \alpha$ as functions of $\tan(\alpha/2)$, and $\tan \alpha'$ as a function of $\tan (\alpha'/2)$, namely

$$\tan \frac{\alpha'}{2} = e^{-u} \tan \frac{\alpha}{2}. \qquad (2\text{-}59)$$

In Fig. 8, Ox is the spatial axis emanating from the point of observation O and parallel to the relative velocity of the object

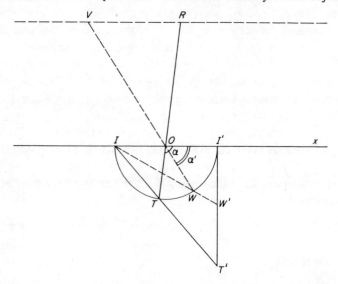

FIG. 8.   Relativistic photography.

to be photographed; R is the position of a point of this object in the system O at the instant when the wave that it emitted reaches O; and V is its position at the earlier instant when it emitted the wave. We shall say that the ensemble of the points R represents the real object at the instant the photograph is taken and the ensemble of the points V represents the virtual object that is photographed. The angles α and α' are as indicated in the figure.

Consider a sphere with center O and arbitrary radius, and let I and I' be its intersections with the axis Ox. In each plane ORV, the lengths $I'T'$ and $I'W'$ are proportional to $\tan(\alpha/2)$ and $\tan(\alpha'/2)$, respectively. Therefore, we pass from T to W by an inversion with pole I and power $(II')^2$, a similitude with pole I' and ratio e^{-u}, and an inversion with pole I and power $(II')^2$. Since this transformation $\mathcal{T}$ conserves angles, the photograph, which we assume to be taken on a spherical plate with center at O, will be "conformal." This will remain true for any object of small apparent diameter photographed perpendicularly onto a plane plate.

A particularly amusing case is that of a perfectly smooth sphere. The cone of revolution with vertex at O and circumscribed about the object R, cuts the sphere of diameter II' in a circle that the transformation $\mathcal{T}$ transforms into a circle. Nevertheless one can show that the object V is not a sphere even though it is inscribed in both a cone of revolution (with vertex at O) and a cylinder of revolution traced out by R.

If the real object is an element of a plane perpendicular to the velocity, the virtual object is cut off by a hyperbolic nappe of revolution with axis Ox and semiangle $\omega = \arctan(1/\sinh u)$. From (56) we have, in fact,

$$x'^2 - (y'^2 + z'^2)\sinh^2 u - 2x'x \cosh u + x^2 = 0.$$

If the real object is an element of a line (of length l) parallel to Ox, the virtual object is also an element of a line (of length l') parallel to Ox, and one can show without much difficulty that

$$l' = l\left(\cosh u - \frac{\cos D}{\cos d}\sinh u\right)^{-1},$$

where $d = (\alpha_2 - \alpha_1)/2$ denotes the apparent semidiameter and $D = (\alpha_1 + \alpha_2)/2$ the mean angle of observation. The "Lorentz contraction in its true size" will thus be photographed if $D = \pi/2$

(as one would expect). On the other hand, there is a direction, such that $\cosh u - (\cos D/\cos d)\sinh u = 1$, in which the object will be photographed in its true size. For objects of very small apparent diameter $(\cos d \approx 1)$ this direction is $D = \arccos [\tanh(u/2)]$.

Figure 9 shows how a rectangular block (real object R) would

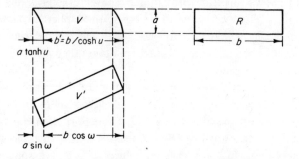

Fig. 9. Relativistic photography: $\sin \omega = \tanh u$, $\cos \omega = 1/\cosh u$.

be photographed (virtual object V) and how, *if its apparent diameter is small*, the object V is visually equivalent to V', i.e., to the real object turned through an angle $\omega = \arccos (1/\cosh u)$ and thus with two sides visible. This last result is deduced most simply if one notices that the photons emanating from the object must be aimed at the position at which the camera will ultimately receive them.

D. Integration and Differentiation in the Kinematics of Continuous Media

2.17 Definitions and Identities

Let $\mathscr{T}$ denote timelike space-time trajectories of a continuous medium, and let us consider *the timelike hyperwall $\mathscr{W}$ of a space-*

time tube of current. This is a three-dimensional manifold generated by the $\mathcal{T}$'s issuing from the whole two-dimensional
boundary surface of a drop of the fluid. We can also consider
the *spacelike hypersections* cutting such a hypertube. These too
are three-dimensional manifolds, and they generalize the classical
concept of "the state of a drop of fluid at an instant t": they are
the *noninstantaneous states* of a drop of fluid. (Each is "instantaneous" in its own rest frame, of course.) E. Cartan, who was
one of the pioneers, exhibited all the consequences that can be
derived from these concepts.[13] Their crucial advantage is that
they guarantee the explicit invariance of the formulas at each
stage of the calculations.

Let us introduce three linearly independent elementary
tangent vectors at a point of a spacelike hypercut, and let
$[dx^j\, dx^k\, dx^l]$ be their exterior product (see §1.11). The dual of this
third rank antisymmetric tensor is a timelike four-vector that we
shall denote by $ic\, du^i$, so that

$$ic\, du^i = \tfrac{1}{6}\varepsilon^{ijkl}[dx_j\, dx_k\, dx_l].\qquad(2\text{-}60)$$

Its fourth component represents the volume in the ordinary
sense, and its three spatial components correspond to *relativistic
corrections for nonsimultaneity*:

$$du^4 = \frac{1}{ic}\,du\,,\qquad du^w = ds^w\, dt\,,\qquad(2\text{-}61)$$

the quantities $ds^w = \tfrac{1}{2}\varepsilon^{uvw}[dx_u\, dx_v]$ denoting, of course, the components of the element of ordinary area.

On the hyperwall $\mathcal{W}$, one of the three vectors above must be
timelike, and we shall take it to be tangent to the local $\mathcal{T}$. The
two others will remain spacelike. The four-vector du^i will then be
spacelike, and its three spatial components will correspond to

[13] "Leçons sur les Invariants Intégraux." Hermann, Paris, 1922.

fluxes per units of surface and time. Its time component will correspond to a relativistic correction for nonsimultaneity.

We shall introduce also the four-dimensional element of volume

$$ic \, d\omega = [dx^1 \, dx^2 \, dx^3 \, dx^4], \qquad (2\text{-}62)$$

which has two useful interpretations. We can look on it as the contracted product of the two four-vectors dx^i (element of trajectory $\mathscr{T}$) and du^i (element of volume on a hypercut). Alternatively, we can think of it as the product of an interval of time dt (affected by the dilatation of durations) and a volume of fluid du (affected by the Lorentz contraction)

$$d\omega = dx^i \, du_i, \qquad d\omega = dt \, du$$
$$(dt = dt_0/\alpha, \qquad du = \alpha \, du_0). \qquad (2\text{-}63)$$

In the relativistic theory of fluids it is often useful to introduce the concept of *proper volume* or *scalar volume*[14]:

$$du_0 = V^i \, du_i. \qquad (2\text{-}64)$$

Integrate this expression over the three-dimensional boundary $\mathscr{C}_2 - \mathscr{C}_1 + \mathscr{W}$ formed by two spacelike hypercuts (similarly oriented with respect to the trajectories $\mathscr{T}$) and the timelike hyperwall of a tube of fluid (Fig. 10). Then, since du_0 is identically zero on $\mathscr{W}$, we obtain, by formula (1-28),

$$u_0(2) - u_0(1) \equiv \Delta u_0 = \int \int \int \int \partial_i V^i \, d\omega, \qquad (2\text{-}65)$$

which is the covariant relativistic generalization of the formula

$$d \, \delta u = \operatorname{div} v \, \delta u \, dt \qquad (2\text{-}66)$$

of classical fluid kinematics.

Incidentally, a reasonable definition of an incompressible fluid in relativity is one for which $du_0 \equiv 0$, or $\partial_i V^i = 0$ (Lichnerowicz' *definition A*).

---

[14] This definition was given by McConnell and Synge, and independently by myself.

Now let Φ be any function of a particle of fluid. As in classical fluid kinematics, we can show that the variation $d\Phi$ is given by

$$d\Phi = V_i \, \partial^i \Phi \, d\tau, \tag{2-67}$$

where $d\tau$ is the proper time.

If Φ is a density, it follows, as before, that

$$\iiint_{\mathscr{C}_2 - \mathscr{C}_1} \Phi V^i \, du_i = \iiiint \partial_i(\Phi V^i) \, d\omega, \tag{2-68}$$

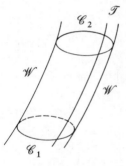

FIG. 10.

or, in infinitesimal form,

$$d(\Phi V^i \, du_i) = \partial_i(\Phi V^i) \, du \, dt. \tag{2-69}$$

We shall be using this formula at the beginning of Chapter 4. We shall also occasionally use the tensor whose 6 independent nonzero components represent the element of space-time surface:

$$ic \, ds^{ij} = \tfrac{1}{2}\varepsilon^{ijkl}\left[dx_k \, dx_l\right]. \tag{2-70}$$

On a timelike hyperwall $\mathscr{W}$

$$du^i = ds^{ij} \, dx_j. \tag{2-71}$$

Chapter 3

RELATIVISTIC ELECTROMAGNETISM

3.1 Introduction

If optics is the root of the theory of relativity, electromagnetism is its trunk. Each of them, for a long time, used the universal constant c that measures the vacuum speed of light. The fundamental equations of the one, as of the other, are invariant under the Lorentz group. Like Molière's Jourdain, the speaker of prose, they had thus long been relativistic without realizing it.

In electromagnetism the concepts of force, energy, and quantity of heat came historically from dynamics and thermodynamics. Electromagnetism is able to define the changes of these entities according to the new kinematics and thus to provide a point of anchorage to relativistic dynamics and thermodynamics. This is important because, historically, dynamics and thermodynamics had ignored the presence and the role of the constant c in their own domains.

As for the definition of a system of units, everyone knows the cruel dilemma of the electrostatic and electromagnetic units in electromagnetism. Since the ratio of the universal constants of the laws of Coulomb and Ampere is c, it is impossible to attribute simultaneously to these two constants the dimensionality of *a pure number* and the numerical value *unity*—at least, not without attributing to c the dimensionality of *a pure number* and the numerical value *unity*. Thus it is only relativistic kinematics that adequately resolves the dilemma of the electrostatic and electromagnetic units—a dilemma that the "mixed system," and even more cleverly the Gaussian system, resolve by deceptive prestidigitation. As for the horrible Giorgi system, conceived before relativity by an engineer who presumably wished "to leave elegance to the tailors" (Boltzmann), it reduces the dilemma to utter confusion.

A. Fundamental Formulas

3.2 General Equations of the Electromagnetic Field

The four equations of the Maxwell–Lorenz–Lorentz[1] field that do not involve the sources are, in a vacuum,

$$\operatorname{curl} \boldsymbol{E} + \frac{1}{c} \frac{\partial}{\partial t} \boldsymbol{H} = 0, \qquad \operatorname{div} \boldsymbol{H} = 0, \qquad (3\text{-}1)$$

where $\boldsymbol{E}$ and $\boldsymbol{H}$ denote respectively the electric and magnetic field intensities. We introduce the antisymmetric space-time tensor E^{ij} of the *Minkowskian electromagnetic field* and its dual (see §1.12) H^{kl} by

$$E^{vw} = iH^{u4} = E^u, \qquad E^{u4} = iH^{vw} = iH^u; \qquad (3\text{-}2)$$

H^{kl} may thus be called the *magnetoelectric field*. There is no difficulty in verifying that Eqs. (1) reduce to either of the two equivalent forms

$$\partial_j E^{ij} = 0, \qquad (3\text{-}3)$$

$$\sum_{\text{cyclic}} \partial^i H^{jk} = 0, \qquad (3\text{-}4)$$

---

[1] It is indeed curious that the outstanding Danish physicist L. Lorenz and the illustrious physicist H. A. Lorentz on several occasions worked in areas so closely related that many formulas validly deserve to be known by both names.

whose very covariance proves that E^{ij} and H^{kl} are indeed the components of two tensors.

From (1) we deduce the existence of the scalar and vector potentials V and A such that

$$H = - \text{curl } A, \qquad E = \text{grad } V + \frac{1}{c} \frac{\partial}{\partial t} A. \qquad (3\text{-}5)$$

Lorenz and Lorentz showed that we can profit from the arbitrariness present in this definition by imposing the condition

$$\text{div } A + \frac{1}{c} \frac{\partial}{\partial t} V = 0. \qquad (3\text{-}6)$$

If to the three components of A we adjoin the quantity

$$A^4 = iV, \qquad (3\text{-}7)$$

Eqs. (5) can be reduced to the form

$$H^{ij} = \partial^j A^i - \partial^i A^j, \qquad (3\text{-}8)$$

which proves that A^i is indeed a four-vector. The Lorenz condition (6) can now be written

$$\partial_i A^i = 0. \qquad (3\text{-}9)$$

In a vacuum the four Maxwell–Lorentz equations that involve sources reduce to

$$\text{curl } H - \frac{1}{c} \frac{\partial}{\partial t} E = j, \qquad \text{div } E = cq, \qquad (3\text{-}10)$$

where j and q denote the current and charge densities. If to the three components of j we now adjoin the quantity j^4 given by

$$j^4 = icq, \qquad (3\text{-}11)$$

the equations (10) reduce to the form

$$\partial_l H^{kl} = j^k, \qquad (3\text{-}12)$$

which shows that j^k is indeed a four-vector.

From (12), using the antisymmetry of the tensor H^{kl}, we deduce that

$$\partial_k j^k = 0,\qquad(3\text{-}13)$$

which is a compact form of the well-known conservation law

$$\operatorname{div} \boldsymbol{j} + \frac{\partial}{\partial t}\, q = 0.\qquad(3\text{-}14)$$

From (8), (9), and (12) we obtain the second order wave equation

$$\Box\, A^k \equiv \partial_l^l A^k = j^k,\qquad(3\text{-}15)$$

where ∂_l^l is a tensorial notation for the well-known d'Alembertian operator

$$\Box \equiv \frac{\partial^2}{\partial x^2} + \frac{\partial^2}{\partial y^2} + \frac{\partial^2}{\partial z^2} - \frac{1}{c^2}\,\frac{\partial^2}{\partial t^2},$$

and from this it follows that

$$\Box\, H^{kl} \equiv \partial_i^i H^{kl} = \partial^l j^k - \partial^k j^l.\qquad(3\text{-}16)$$

3.3 Invariance and Conservation of Electric Charge

In the theory of Lorentz, the electric current source term is assumed to be purely convective, and one writes

$$j^u = q v^u,\qquad j^4 = i c q,\qquad(3\text{-}17)$$

where v^u is the ordinary velocity of the charged fluid. If we introduce the *proper value*, q_0, of the charge density, i.e., the value of q in the instantaneously co-moving local Lorentz frame, so that

$$q = \frac{q_0}{\sqrt{1 - \beta^2}},\qquad(3\text{-}18)$$

and if we take account of the definition (2-39) of the four-velocity, we can write (17) in the covariant form

$$j^l = q_0 V^l.\qquad(3\text{-}19)$$

Let δu^k be the four-vector representing a small element of volume defined as in (2-60), and let δu_0 be the *proper scalar volume* defined as in (2-64) by means of the velocity field V^i. Consider the tensorial invariant

$$\delta Q = j^k \, \delta u_k, \qquad (3\text{-}20)$$

which may be written also as

$$\delta Q = q_0 \, \delta u_0. \qquad (3\text{-}21)$$

If we use the instantaneously co-moving frame ($j^u = 0$), or indeed, if we integrate for a constant time ($\delta u^u = 0$), the expression (20) reduces to $q \, \delta u$. All this shows that the scalar δQ is the relativistic expression of the *element of electric charge*.

In the general case we have, by (2-61),

$$\delta Q = q \, \delta u + j^u \, \delta s_u \, dt, \qquad (3\text{-}22)$$

where the last three terms, $j^u \, \delta s_u \, dt$, represent a *flux of electricity* that must be taken into account if the material droplet is considered in a nonsimultaneous manner. If the element of volume δu_k is relative to the lateral wall $\mathscr{W}$ of a space-time tube of current, the expression $j^k \, \delta u_k$ is identically zero in the convective case considered here.[2]

Finally, if we integrate the expression (20) over a domain bounded by the hyperwall $\mathscr{W}$ of a tube of fluid and two spacelike hypercuts $\mathscr{C}_1$ and $\mathscr{C}_2$ representing an initial state and a final state of the charged material drop, we obtain, because of (13),

$$\iiint\!\!\int \partial_k j^k \, \delta\omega \equiv 0, \qquad (3\text{-}23)$$

and as a result, in the convective case considered here,

$$Q_2 - Q_1 = 0, \qquad (3\text{-}24)$$

---

[2] See Fig. 10. If there were conduction within the matter, the quantity $j^k \, \delta u_k$, if nonzero on $\mathscr{W}$, would represent the flux of electricity.

where

$$Q = \int \int_{\mathscr{C}} \int j^k \, \delta u_k. \qquad (3\text{-}25)$$

This is the integral expression of the law of conservation of charge, of which (13) is the differential representation.

3.4   Retarded Potentials

It is well known that equations of the type (15) admit the retarded solutions of Kirchhoff that are written in classical form as

$$A^k(r_0, t_0) = \frac{1}{4\pi} \int \int \int j^k \left(r_0 - r, t_0 - \frac{r}{c} \right) \frac{\delta u}{r}. \qquad (3\text{-}26)$$

The expression $\delta u / r$ is a relativistic invariant, being the ratio of corresponding components of two collinear isotropic four-vectors.

Let us show how we can go from Kirchhoff's formula to the Liénard–Wiechert formula for a point charge. If V^i is any four-vector, we can write

$$\frac{\delta u}{r} = \frac{V^i \, \delta u_i}{V^j r_j}. \qquad (3\text{-}27)$$

If V^i is the four-velocity of the fluid, and thus collinear with j^i in the convective case, we have

$$j^k \frac{V^i \, \delta u_i}{V^j r_j} = V^k \frac{j^i \, \delta u_i}{V^j r_j} = \frac{V^k \, \delta Q}{V^j r_j}, \qquad (3\text{-}28)$$

and from this by constricting the filament of fluid, we obtain

$$4\pi A^k = \frac{Q V^k}{r_i V^i} = \frac{Q \, dx^k}{r_i \, dx^i}, \qquad (3\text{-}29)$$

which is the covariant form of the Liénard–Wiechert formula

whose classical form is

$$4\pi A = \frac{(Q/c)\,\boldsymbol{v}}{(r - \boldsymbol{r}\cdot\boldsymbol{\beta})_{t-r/c}}, \qquad 4\pi V = \frac{Q}{(r - \boldsymbol{r}\cdot\boldsymbol{\beta})_{t-r/c}}\,. \qquad (3\text{-}30)$$

3.5   Force: as Density and in Finite Form

We recall the classical expression for the density of the Lorentz force and its consequence:

$$\boldsymbol{f} = q\,(c\boldsymbol{E} + \boldsymbol{v}\times\boldsymbol{H}), \qquad \boldsymbol{f}\cdot\boldsymbol{v} = cq\,\boldsymbol{v}\cdot\boldsymbol{E}\,. \qquad (3\text{-}31)$$

If we make the single assumption that

$$f^4 = \frac{i}{c}\boldsymbol{f}\cdot\boldsymbol{v} = i\,\boldsymbol{f}\cdot\boldsymbol{\beta}\,, \qquad (3\text{-}32)$$

these formulas reduce to

$$f^k = H^{kl}j_l\,, \qquad (3\text{-}33)$$

which shows that f^k is a four-vector. From (32), or (33) together with (19), we obtain

$$V_k f^k = 0 \qquad (3\text{-}34)$$

which shows that the four-vector f^k is spacelike.[3]

For a point charge Q we have the well-known expression for the finite Lorentz force and its consequence

$$\mathfrak{F} = Q\,(c\,\boldsymbol{E} + \boldsymbol{v}\times\boldsymbol{H}), \qquad \mathfrak{F}\cdot\boldsymbol{v} = cQ\,\boldsymbol{v}\cdot\boldsymbol{E}\,, \qquad (3\text{-}35)$$

but these formulas are not covariant in this form.

Therefore we write

$$d\boldsymbol{p} = \mathfrak{F}\,dt\,, \qquad dp^4 = \frac{i}{c}\,\mathfrak{F}\cdot d\boldsymbol{M} = \frac{i}{c}\,\mathfrak{F}\cdot\boldsymbol{v}\,dt\,, \qquad (3\text{-}36)$$

[3] Formula (34) is no longer valid if there is conduction. For further details see §3.7.

and obtain from (35) and (36) the covariant formula

$$dp^k = QH^{kl}\, dx_l, \qquad (3\text{-}37)$$

which shows that dp^k is a four-vector. It is the *four-vector element of momentum-energy* furnished by the field to the point charge. The antisymmetric tensor

$$F^{kl} = QH^{kl} \qquad (3\text{-}38)$$

may well be called the *space-time Lorentz force*. We have shown [4] that this type of definition of the finite force is valid under quite general conditions.

As an exercise, the reader may investigate the covariant relationship that exists between the definitions (33) and (38).[5]

From (8) and (37) we obtain

$$dP^k = -\, Q\, \partial^k A^l\, dx_l, \qquad (3\text{-}39)$$

where

$$P^k = p^k - QA^k. \qquad (3\text{-}40)$$

The quantity $-QA^k$ is, by definition, the potential electromagnetic *momentum-energy* that combines additively with the *kinematic or proper momentum-energy* [6] of the particle to give the *total momentum-energy*. Formula (39) is the basic formula on which is built the whole of relativistic analytical mechanics.[7]

3.6 The Maxwell Tensor

From the general Maxwell–Lorentz equations (33), (12), and

[4] *Compt. Rend.* **221,** 743 (1945).

[5] This relationship, which is not trivial, is explained in our *Théorie de la Relativité Restreinte.*

[6] See §4.5.

[7] See §5.1.

(3), we obtain
$$f^i = -H^{ik} \, \partial^j H_{jk} + E^{ik} \, \partial^j E_{jk}.$$

But we can verify the identities
$$E^{ik}E_k^j + H^{ik}H_k^j = \tfrac{1}{2}E^{kl}E_{kl}\,\delta^{ij} = \tfrac{1}{2}H^{kl}H_{kl}\,\delta^{ij},$$

the tensors E and H being duals of one another, and from these two formulas and the definition
$$M^{ij} = \tfrac{1}{2}\big(E^{ik}E_k^j - H^{ik}H_k^j\big) \tag{3-41}$$

we obtain the formula
$$f^i = \partial_j M^{ij}, \tag{3-42}$$

which allows us to interpret the *Maxwell tensor* (41) as a *formal elastic stress tensor* linked to the electromagnetic field.

It is interesting to analyze the content of this tensor. The 9 spatial components
$$M^{uv} = E^u E^v + H^u H^v - \tfrac{1}{2}\big(E^2 + H^2\big)\,\delta^{uv} \tag{3-43}$$

represent the Maxwell stress tensor in the original sense of the term. The 6 components
$$M^{u4} = M^{4u} = \mathrm{i}\,[E \times H]^{vw} \tag{3-44}$$

represent the Poynting *momentum density* or *density of energy flux*. And finally, the component
$$M^{44} = -\tfrac{1}{2}(E^2 + H^2) = -w \tag{3-45}$$

represents, except for sign, the *energy density of the field*.

It should be noted that since the tensor $\mathscr{M}^{ij}$ is defined in (42) only to within an additive tensor of zero divergence, we can not exclude *a priori* the presence of additive constants in (43), (44), and (45).

In the general case in which inductions are present, the Maxwell–Minkowski tensor becomes asymmetric, and we have to add a complementary term to formula (42).[8]

[8] See §3.9.

B.   Further Developments

3.7   Case in Which There Is Conduction. Laplace Force and Joule Heat

When a conducting body, represented kinematically by a four-velocity field $V^k(x^i)$, is traversed by a current of density j^k, we write with Minkowski

$$j^k = j'^k + j''^k, \tag{3-46}$$

where

$$j'^k = -c^{-2}V_l j^l V^k, \qquad V_k j''^k = 0. \tag{3-47}$$

The total current j^k is thus decomposed into a timelike *convection current* j'^k and a spacelike *conduction current* j''^k. The classical expression for the density of the Laplace force is

$$f'' = j'' \times H \tag{3-48}$$

and experiment shows that this force density is applied to the conducting matter. The covariant form of (48) is evidently

$$f''^k = H^{kl} j''_l. \tag{3-49}$$

Since j''^k, which is spacelike, is not collinear with the four-velocity V^k, we have

$$V_k f''^k \neq 0, \qquad \text{or} \qquad f^4 \neq i f \cdot \beta, \tag{3-50}$$

which entails important consequences, as we shall see.

If the resistivity of the matter under consideration is denoted by $r(x^i)$, the classical expression of Ohm's law is

$$E = cr j'', \tag{3-51}$$

and we see, with Minkowski, that the only covariant formula corresponding to (51) (on the assumption that r is a space-time scalar) is

$$V_l H^{kl} = r j''^k. \tag{3-52}$$

If Joule's universal constant is denoted by J, the classical expression for the quantity of heat $d\,\delta\mathcal{Q}$ generated in volume δu in time dt is such that

$$J\,d\,\delta\mathcal{Q} = rj''^2\,\delta u\,dt\,. \qquad (3\text{-}53)$$

The corresponding covariant expression can be written immediately, taking account of the definition (2-63), as

$$J\,d\,\delta\mathcal{Q} = rj''_k j''^k\,d\omega\,. \qquad (3\text{-}54)$$

The heat $\mathcal{Q}$ is thus defined as a space-time scalar.[9]

From (49) and (52) we obtain

$$V_k f''^k = -\,rj''_k j''^k \qquad (3\text{-}55)$$

so that (54) can be written

$$J\,d\mathcal{Q} = -\,V_k f''^k\,d\omega\,. \qquad (3\text{-}56)$$

The generation of Joule heat is thus put into the form of work done by the force density f''^k in space-time.[10]

3.8   Case in Which There Is Electromagnetic Polarization

We know that a dielectric medium is characterized by a density of electrical polarization P and that a magnetic medium is characterized by a density of magnetic polarization M. Thus, along with the electric and magnetic fields E and H, we have to introduce the electric and magnetic inductions D and B such that

$$D = E + P\,, \qquad B = H + M\,. \qquad (3\text{-}57)$$

The Maxwell equations (1), (3), (31), and (35) must then be

---

[9] We can also bring in the definition of a "calorific momentum-heat four-vector" $d\,\delta\mathcal{Q}^k$ such that $V_k\,\delta\mathcal{Q}^k = -\,c^2\,\delta\mathcal{Q}$. For this purpose it suffices to introduce the notion of a "conductivity four-vector" $r^{-1}V_k$.

[10] See Pauli, "Theory of Relativity," pp. 107–108. Pergamon Press, Oxford, 1958.

written with the substitution $H \rightarrow B$, while (10) and their consequences must be written with the substitution $E \rightarrow D$. The postulate of the covariance of electromagnetism then requires that we write, with Minkowski, the following definitions of the *density of magnetoelectric polarization tensor* M^{ij} and its dual P^{kl} ($u, v = 1, 2, 3$):

$$M^{vw} = iP^{u4} = M^u, \qquad M^{u4} = iP^{vw} = iP^u, \qquad (3\text{-}58)$$

as well as those of the *electric field-magnetic induction tensor*

$$E^{vw} = iB^{u4} = E^u, \qquad E^{u4} = iB^{vw} = iB^u; \qquad (3\text{-}59)$$

and those of the *magnetic field-electric induction*

$$D^{vw} = iH^{u4} = D^u, \qquad D^{u4} = iH^{vw} = iH^u. \qquad (3\text{-}60)$$

With these we can rewrite the definition formulas (57) in the covariant form

$$B^{ij} = H^{ij} + M^{ij}, \qquad D^{ij} = E^{ij} + P^{ij}. \qquad (3\text{-}61)$$

The fundamental formulas (3) and (12) of Maxwell retain the same form, but (8) has to be replaced by

$$B^{ij} = \partial^j A^i - \partial^i A^j \qquad (3\text{-}62)$$

and (33) by

$$f^k = B^{kl} j_l \qquad (3\text{-}63)$$

or (37) by[11]

$$dp^k = QB^{kl} \, dx_l. \qquad (3\text{-}64)$$

We have to modify formulas (15) and (16) by the substitution $j^k \rightarrow j^k_{(m)}$, where

$$j^k_{(m)} = \partial_l B^{kl} \qquad (3\text{-}65)$$

and represents the "mean" or "macroscopic current." We write

---

[11] It is in a way unfortunate that the terminology sanctified by long usage should give rise, in formulas (59) and (60), to the association of a *field* and an *induction*. L. Arzeliès, arguing on the ground that a *field* multiplied by a physical intensity (charge, current, etc.) gives rise to a *force*, proposes the interchange of the labels *magnetic field* and *magnetic induction*.

$$j^k_{(p)} = \partial_l M^{kl},\qquad\qquad (3\text{-}66)$$

representing the "polarization current," and as a result we have

$$j^k_{(m)} = j^k + j^k_{(p)}.\qquad\qquad (3\text{-}67)$$

There also exists, in principle, a macroscopic magnetic current density $l^k_{(m)}$ that happens to be equal to the polarization current density $l^k_{(p)}$. Unlike $\partial_l E^{kl}$, the expressions $\partial_l P^{kl}$ and $\partial_l D^{kl}$ are therefore, in general, not zero:

$$l^k_{(m)} = \partial_l D^{kl},\qquad l^k_{(p)} = \partial_l P^{kl},\qquad \partial_l D^{kl} = \partial_l P^{kl}.\qquad (3\text{-}68)$$

A final point to be considered is the covariant definition of the susceptibility. Clearly, the only possible form is

$$P^{ij} = \varepsilon^{ij\,kl}_{\smile\smile} B_{kl},\qquad\qquad (3\text{-}69)$$

where $\varepsilon^{ij\,kl}_{\smile\smile}$ denotes a tensor antisymmetric in ij and in kl that we can assume symmetric under interchange of the pairs of indices ij and kl.[12]

3.9   Case in Which There Is Polarization (Continued). Asymmetry of the Momentum-Energy Tensor

In order to simplify the writing of future formulas we shall extend a notational convention due to Jauch and Rohrlich[13] by writing

$$[\partial_i] = \partial_i - \varrho_i,\qquad\qquad (3\text{-}70)$$

where ϱ_i denotes the partial differentiation operator acting to the *left*: $F(x^j)\,\varrho_i \equiv \partial_i F(x^j)$.

If we perform the calculations once more that lead to the formulas (41) and (42), this time taking account of (63), (3), and

[12] On this subject see the remarks of E. J. Post, "Formal Structure of Electromagnetics," p. 127 ff. North-Holland Publ., Amsterdam, 1962.

[13] "The Theory of Photons and Electrons," pp. 53–54. Addison-Wesley, Reading, Massachusetts, 1955.

(12), we obtain

$$f^{i}_{(1)} \equiv B^{ik}j_k + \tfrac{1}{4}B^{kl}\left[\partial^i\right]H_{kl} = \partial_j \mathscr{M}^{ij}, \tag{3-71}$$

where $\mathscr{M}^{ij}$ is the *asymmetric Maxwell–Minkowski tensor*, defined by

$$\begin{aligned}\mathscr{M}^{ij} &= \tfrac{1}{2}\left[D^{ik}E^{j}_{k} - B^{ik}H^{j}_{k}\right]\\ &= -B^{ik}H^{j}_{k} + \tfrac{1}{4}B^{kl}H_{kl}\,\delta^{ij}.\end{aligned} \tag{3-72}$$

Thus when polarization is present the total force density, which arises from the "elastic tensor" $\mathscr{M}^{ij}$, involves in addition to the *Lorentz force density* (63) another term recognized for the first time by Minkowski.

The significance of this term will be more apparent if we change the definitions slightly:

$$f^{*i}_{(1)} \equiv B^{ik}j_k + \tfrac{1}{2}B^{kl}\,\partial^i H_{kl} \equiv \partial_j \mathscr{M}^{*ij}, \tag{3-71'}$$

$$\mathscr{M}^{*ij} \equiv -B^{ik}H^{j}_{k}. \tag{3-72'}$$

The term $\tfrac{1}{2}B^{kl}\,\partial^i H_{kl}$ in (71') is the *force density* applied to a polarized medium by an inhomogeneous field (since if $M^{kl} \gg H^{kl}$, $B^{kl} \approx M^{kl}$).

It is interesting to examine the contents of the tensor $\mathscr{M}^{ij}$ in detail. The 9 components

$$\mathscr{M}^{uv} = E^{u}D^{v} + H^{u}B^{v} - \tfrac{1}{2}(\boldsymbol{E}\cdot\boldsymbol{D} + \boldsymbol{B}\cdot\boldsymbol{H})\,\delta^{uv} \tag{3-73}$$

are those of the classical asymmetric "elastic" tensor of Maxwell and Heaviside. The 2×3 components with indices $u4$ and $4u$ represent two Poynting vectors

$$\mathscr{M}^{u4} = \mathrm{i}\left[\boldsymbol{D}\times\boldsymbol{B}\right]^{vw} \tag{3-74}$$

$$\mathscr{M}^{4u} = \mathrm{i}\left[\boldsymbol{E}\times\boldsymbol{H}\right]^{vw}, \tag{3-75}$$

the first of which is interpreted as the *momentum density* and the second as the *current of energy density* of the field. Finally, the component

$$\mathscr{M}^{44} = -\tfrac{1}{2}(\boldsymbol{E}\cdot\boldsymbol{D} + \boldsymbol{B}\cdot\boldsymbol{H}) = -w \tag{3-76}$$

represents the classical *energy density* of the field.

Note that
$$\mathcal{M}_i^i = 0, \tag{3-77}$$

showing that the proper energy density of the field is zero.

Because of the asymmetry of the tensor $\mathcal{M}^{ij}$, the two expressions

$$P^i = \int\int\int_\mathscr{C} \mathcal{M}^{ij}\, du_j \tag{3-78}$$

and

$$L^i = \int\int\int_\mathscr{C} \mathcal{M}^{ji}\, du_j \tag{3-79}$$

are not equal. The significance of this will become clear in the light of the theory of the spin (see §4.11). The four-vector $T^i \equiv P^i - L^i$ is to be regarded as a potential *momentum-energy* such that the expression $\partial T/\partial t$ is equivalent to a force (Abraham).

In the classical theory of elasticity, the antisymmetric tensor (cf. (1-21) and (1-22))
$$\mu^{uv} = \mathcal{M}^{uv}_\smile \tag{3-80}$$

represents a ponderomotive couple density. Analogously, we shall say here that the antisymmetric tensor

$$\mu^{ij} = \mathcal{M}^{ij}_\smile \tag{3-81}$$

represents a *space-time torque density*. Its three components (cf. (72) and (60))
$$\mu^{uv} = [E \times P + B \times M]^{uv} \tag{3-82}$$

represent the classical couple density applied by the fields E and H to a medium having polarizations P and M. The three other components

$$\mu^{u4} = -\,\mathrm{i}\,[D \times B - E \times H]^{vw} \equiv \mathrm{i}\,[B \times P - E \times M]^{vw} \tag{3-83}$$

are an expression of the quantity

$$T^i = P^i - L^i = \int\int\int_\mathscr{C} \mu^{ij}\, du_j \tag{3-84}$$

calculated for a fixed time, while $\partial\mu^{u4}/\partial t$ is the Abraham force density.[14]

In addition to the Maxwell tensor $\mathcal{M}^{ij}$ we can introduce two other asymmetric elastic tensors $\mathcal{N}^{ij}$ and $\mathcal{T}^{ij}$ that appear in the Dirac theory of the electron and in quantum field theory.

From (63) and (62) we easily deduce that

$$f^i_{(2)} \equiv B^{ik}j_k + \tfrac{1}{2}j^k[\partial^i]A_k = \partial_j\mathcal{N}^{ij}, \qquad (3\text{-}85)$$

with

$$\mathcal{N}^{kl} = A^kj^l - \tfrac{1}{2}A^ij_i\,\delta^{kl}, \qquad (3\text{-}86)$$

or, as in the case of the Maxwell tensor,

$$f^{*i}_{(2)} \equiv B^{ik}j_k + j^k\,\partial^iA_k = \partial_j\mathcal{N}^{*ij}, \qquad (3\text{-}85')$$

with

$$\mathcal{N}^{*kl} = A^kj^l. \qquad (3\text{-}86')$$

Multiplying (85') by $d\omega = du_l\,dx^l$, taking dx^l collinear with j^l, and using (86'), we bring (85') to the form (39) and (40), which we rewrite

$$QB^{ij}\,dx_j - Q\,\partial^iA^j\,dx_j = Q\,dA^i.$$

The first term corresponds to the Lorentz force, and the second has a structure *analogous* to that of the force applied to a polarized body by an inhomogeneous field. Neither this term nor the right-hand side is gage invariant.

We list the contents of the tensor $\mathcal{N}^{*ij}$ and its trace in detail:

$$\begin{aligned} \mathcal{N}^{*uv} &= A^uj^v, & \mathcal{N}^{*44} &= -cVq, \\ \mathcal{N}^{*u4} &= icqA^u, & \mathcal{N}^{*4u} &= iVj^u, \\ \mathcal{N}^{*i}_i &= A^kj_k = A\cdot j - cVq. \end{aligned} \qquad (3\text{-}87)$$

Also, for the torque density

$$v^{kl} = \mathcal{N}^{kl}_\smile = A^kj^l - A^lj^k \qquad (3\text{-}88)$$

we have

$$v^{uv} = [A\times j]^{uv}, \qquad v^{u4} = i(cqA - Vj)^u. \qquad (3\text{-}89)$$

[14] See Pauli, "Theory of Relativity," p. 110. Pergamon Press, Oxford, 1958. An operational discussion of the physical interpretation of $D\times B$ as distinct from $E\times H$, and thus also of μ^{u4} in Eq. (83) and T^i in Eq. (84), is given by us in *Compt. Rend.* **261**, 4637 (1965).

All these expressions arise, with appropriate physical significance, in the Dirac theory of the electron and quantum field theory.

The relation between the tensors $\mathcal{M}$ and $\mathcal{N}$ is made plain if we introduce the momentum-energy tensor defined by Louis de Broglie in his theory of the photon,[15]

$$\mathcal{T}^{ij} = \tfrac{1}{2} H^{jk} [\partial^i] A_k, \tag{3-90}$$

whose trace has the value

$$\mathcal{T}^i_i = \tfrac{1}{2} j^k A_k - \tfrac{1}{4} B^{kl} H_{kl}. \tag{3-91}$$

It is such that

$$\partial_j \mathcal{T}^{ij} = \tfrac{1}{4} M^{kl} [\partial^i] H_{kl} - \tfrac{1}{2} j^k [\partial^i] A_k = f^i_{(1)} - f^i_{(2)}. \tag{3-92}$$

From (71), (85), and (91) we obtain

$$\partial_j \mathcal{T}^{ij} = \partial_j (\mathcal{M}^{ij} - \mathcal{N}^{ij}). \tag{3-93}$$

In de Broglie's theory of the photon,[15] the "proper angular momentum density" or "spin density" is given by[16]

$$\sigma^{ijk} = \sum_{\text{cyclic}} H^{ij} A^k. \tag{3-94}$$

Using Maxwell's equations and the preceding definitions, we find

$$\overset{\vee}{\mathcal{T}}{}^{ij} + \partial_k \sigma^{ijk} = \partial_j (\overset{\vee}{\mathcal{M}}{}^{ij} - \overset{\vee}{\mathcal{N}}{}^{ij}) \tag{3-95}$$

and therefore, in empty space,

$$\overset{\vee}{\mathcal{T}}{}^{ij} + \partial_k \sigma^{ijk} = 0. \tag{3-96}$$

We shall see (§4.11) that this relation between the antisymmetric part of the momentum-energy tensor and the spin density has an excellent physical interpretation.

[15] "La Mécanique Ondulatoire du Photon." Vol. 1, pp. 185–192. Hermann, Paris, 1940; or "Mécanique Ondulatoire du Photon et Théorie Quantique des Champs," pp. 43–44. Gauthier-Villars, Paris, 1949.

[16] E. Henriot, "Les Couples de Radiation et les Moments Electromagnetiques." Gauthiers-Villars, Paris, 1936. He was apparently the first to point out the presence of spin σ^{ijk} in classical electromagnetism.

Chapter 4

RELATIVISTIC DYNAMICS

4.1 Introduction

In the classical theory of relativity, dynamics is subordinated to electromagnetism in that the kinematic changes in force and energy were made precise by means of electromagnetism.[1]

The appearance—unsuspected by the classical theorists—of the constant c in dynamics gives rise to new effects: a kinematic law of variation of the mass of a particle as a function of the speed, and, above all, the discovery of a universal proportionality between mass and energy, the ratio being c^2.

Following von Laue, we prefer to present relativistic dynamics by starting with the case of continuous media since it is via this route that the number of postulates required is the least.

---

[1] This subordination of dynamics to electromagnetism disappears if we introduce wave mechanics, (in the de Broglie form rather than the non-relativistic Schrödinger form) at the very beginning, immediately after the kinematic definition of the wave number-frequency four-vector. Of wave mechanics (where the constant c plays an essential role) one can say what was said above about electromagnetism: that it is *essentially* relativistic. In wave mechanics, electromagnetism is merely a particular case of general mechanics, namely the *theory of the photon*.

A. General Formulas

4.2 Résumé of the Fundamental Formulas of the Newtonian Dynamics of Continuous Media

Consider a material droplet of mass m moving with velocity v, and let $\mathfrak{F}$ be the resultant of the applied forces (assumed to be purely volume forces), dM the elementary displacement of the center of mass, and $\mathfrak{F}\,dt$ and dW the elementary variations of the applied impulse and the acquired energy. Then

$$\mathfrak{F}\,dt = d(m\,v), \qquad \mathfrak{F}\cdot dM = dW. \tag{4-1}$$

If we introduce the densities f, ρ, w corresponding respectively to $\mathfrak{F}$, m, W, by

$$\delta m = \rho\,\delta u, \qquad \delta\mathfrak{F} = f\,\delta u, \qquad \delta W = w\,\delta u, \tag{4-2}$$

where δu is the volume of the droplet at time t, the fundamental formulas (1) may be written

$$f\,\delta u\,dt = d(\rho v\,\delta u), \qquad f\cdot v\,\delta u\,dt = d(w\,\delta u). \tag{4-3}$$

Now, from the two well-known formulas

$$d\Phi = (v^u\,\partial_u\Phi + \partial_t\Phi)\,dt$$

and

$$d(\delta u) = \partial_u v^u \cdot \delta u\,dt,$$

where $u = 1, 2, 3$, and $\partial_t \equiv \partial/\partial t$, we deduce

$$d(\Phi\,\delta u) = [\partial_u(\Phi v^u) + \partial_t\Phi]\,\delta u\,dt$$

(which is the prerelativistic form of the formula (2-69)).

On successively setting $\Phi = \rho v$ and $\Phi = w$ in this formula we obtain from (4-3)

$$\begin{aligned} f^u &= \partial_v(\rho v^u v^v) + \partial_t(\rho v^u), \\ f\cdot v &= \partial_u(w v^u) + \delta_t(w), \end{aligned} \tag{4-4}$$

where $u, v = 1, 2, 3$.

4.3 Fundamental Formulas of the Relativistic Dynamics of Continuous Media

From the theory of the Lorentz force density in electromagnetism we know (formula (3-32)) that the quantity

$$f^4 = \frac{i}{c} f \cdot v \tag{4-5}$$

is the fourth component of a space-time vector whose first three components are f^u. The $16 = 9 + 3 + 3 + 1$ quantities $\rho v^u v^v$, ρv^u, $w v^u$, w are thus the components of a second rank space-time tensor whose precise definition is

$$T^{uv} = T^{vu} = \rho v^u v^v,$$

$$T^{u4} = ic\rho v^u, \qquad T^{4u} = \frac{i}{c} w v^u, \tag{4-6}$$

$$T^{44} = -c^2 \rho.$$

This is the tensor of the *momentum-energy density*, called briefly the *momentum-energy tensor*. In terms of the definition (5) and (6), the fundamental formulas (4) reduce to the form

$$f^i = \partial_j T^{ij}, \tag{4-7}$$

where $i, j, = 1, 2, 3, 4$.

It is easy to see[2] that the essential symmetry of the 9 components $\rho v^u v^v$ implies the complete symmetry of the tensor T^{ij}. If we write

$$T^{u4} = T^{4u}$$

we obtain (in terms of density) the relativistic law of universal equivalence of energy and mass:

$$w = c^2 \rho. \tag{4-8}$$

Substituting this expression for w in the fourth equation of (4)

[2] We leave it as a simple exercise for the reader.

we obtain
$$\partial_u(\rho v^u) + \partial_t(\rho) = c^{-2} \mathbf{f} \cdot \mathbf{v}, \qquad (4\text{-}9)$$

which replaces the classical equation of continuity

$$\partial_u(\rho v^u) + \partial_t(\rho) = 0 \qquad (4\text{-}9')$$

(obtained from (2-69) and (4-2) on postulating the conservation of the mass δm of the fluid droplet). The difference between the classical and relativistic theories is thus, here also, of the second order in $1/c$. The second term of (9) represents the *density of the power* applied to the fluid, which is *relative* to the reference frame being used. In particular, it is zero in the locally co-moving frame.

Let us recapitulate the postulates implicit in the preceding derivation.

In the first formula (1) we include m inside the parentheses so as to be able to free ourselves from the classical postulate $m = \text{const}$. This freedom was exploited in the classical formulas (4) in conjunction with the relativistic formula (5).

As for this formula (5), it implies, as we know, the restrictive hypothesis (3-34), which we rewrite as

$$V_i f^i = 0, \qquad (4\text{-}10)$$

V^i always denoting the four-velocity.

The introduction of the four-velocity allows us to reduce the definitions (6) to the form

$$T^{ij} = \rho_0 V^i V^j, \qquad (4\text{-}11)$$

where ρ_0 denotes the *density of proper mass* of the fluid, i.e., the value of ρ in the locally co-moving reference frame.

Between ρ and ρ_0 (and, of course, w and w_0) we have the relations

$$\rho = \frac{\rho_0}{1-\beta^2}, \qquad w = \frac{w_0}{1-\beta^2}, \qquad (4\text{-}12)$$

the factor $1/\sqrt{1-\beta^2}$ entering twice in each case, once because of the change of mass with speed and once because of the change of volume.

Contracting the tensor T^{ij} and remembering that $V_i V^i = -c^2$, we have

$$T = T_i^i = -c^2 \rho_0 = \rho(v^2 - c^2).$$ (4-13)

If we calculate the expression (7) using the form (11), and multiply by V_i and contract, using (10) and the facts that $V^j \, \partial_j V^i = dV^i/d\tau = V'^i$ and $V_i V'^i = 0$, we find that

$$\partial_j(\rho_0 V^j) = 0,$$ (4-14)

and thus that

$$f^i = \rho_0 V'^i.$$ (4-15)

Formula (14) expresses the relativistic law of conservation of the proper mass of the fluid. It results from our having made two very restrictive hypotheses: (1) the absence of surface forces, and (2) the absence of work done by the force density f^i (formula (10)).[3]

As for formula (15), which is valid under the same restrictive hypotheses, it is the manifest extension of the classical formula $f = \rho \gamma$, where γ is the acceleration vector.

4.4 Integral Formulas

Let us take quadruple integrals of both sides of formula (7):

$$\iiiint f^i \, d\omega = \iiiint \partial_j T^{ij} \, d\omega.$$ (4-16)

With the form (11) of the momentum-energy tensor there exists a four-velocity field, and so, as in §§2.17 and 3.3, we can use the four-dimensional domain bounded by a hyperwall, $\mathscr{W}$, of a tube of current and two hypercuts, $\mathscr{C}_1$, and $\mathscr{C}_2$ (see Fig. 10, p. 51).

---

[3] To see how the lifting of either of these restrictions modifies formula (14) see §§4.7 and 4.8.

The integrand
$$f^i \, d\omega = f^i \, \delta u \, dt$$

of the first term obviously represents the *ponderomotive momentum-energy* $f \, \delta u \, dt$, $(i/c) \, f \, \delta u \cdot d\mathbf{M}$ communicated to the material volume δu in time dt.

The second term can be transformed by means of the general formula (1-28) into the triple integral

$$\iint\limits_{\mathscr{C}_2 - \mathscr{C}_1 + \mathscr{W}} \int T^{ij} \, \delta u_j$$

taken over the boundary of the four-dimensional domain. Because of (11), the contribution of $\mathscr{W}$ is zero (as in §§2.17 and 3.3) and there remains (using (2-64)),

$$\iint\limits_{\mathscr{C}_2 - \mathscr{C}_1} \int T^{ij} \, \delta u_j = \iint\limits_{\mathscr{C}_2 - \mathscr{C}_1} \int \rho_0 V^i V^j \, \delta u_j$$

$$= \iint\limits_{\mathscr{C}_2 - \mathscr{C}_1} \int \rho_0 V^i \, \delta u_0 .$$

The second term thus represents the *change in the dynamical momentum-energy* of the material droplet in the course of its motion from the state $\mathscr{C}_1$ to the state $\mathscr{C}_2$.[4]

To sum up, the integral expression of the fundamental formula of dynamics is, in the present case,

$$\iint\int\int f^i \, d\omega = \iint\limits_{\mathscr{C}_2 - \mathscr{C}_1} \int \rho_0 V^i \, \delta u_0 . \tag{4-17}$$

It equates the ponderomotive and inertial, or dynamical, ex-

---

[4] Even more explicitly, we can calculate the triple integrals at a particular time, in which case only the component $\delta u^4 = - (i/c) \, \delta u$ differs from zero. On referring to the formulas (6), one thus obtains ($u = 1, 2, 3$):

$$p^u = \iiint \rho v^u \, \delta u \qquad \text{and} \qquad p^t = ic \iiint \rho \, \delta u = ic \iiint \delta m.$$

pressions of the change in the momentum-energy of the portion of matter under consideration.

Incidentally, a similar procedure applied to formula (14) leads to the result

$$\iiint\limits_{\mathscr{C}_2-\mathscr{C}_1} \rho_0 V^i \, \delta u_i = \iiint\limits_{\mathscr{C}_2-\mathscr{C}_1} \rho_0 \, \delta u_0 = 0, \qquad (4\text{-}18)$$

which is the integral expression of the conservation of rest mass implied by the present hypotheses.[5]

Finally, if dx^i denotes an element of a space-time trajectory of matter, the expression

$$\delta p^i \, dx_i = \rho_0 V^i V^j \, dx_i \, \delta u_j$$
$$= \rho_0 V^i V_i \, dx^j \, \delta u_j = -c^2 \rho_0 \, \delta\omega \qquad (4\text{-}19)$$

obviously represents the Hamiltonian action per element of volume and time. So in integral form, we have

$$\mathscr{A} = -c^2 \iiiint \rho_0 \, \delta\omega. \qquad (4\text{-}20)$$

4.5 Fundamental Formulas of Particle Dynamics

Retaining the same hypotheses (absence of surface forces, and orthogonality of the four-vectors V^i and f^i), let us apply formulas (17) and (18) to the case of an infinitely narrow world tube, writing

$$\lim \iiint \rho_0 \, \delta u_0 = m_0 = \text{const}, \qquad (4\text{-}21)$$

$$\lim \iiint f^i \, \delta u_0 = F^i. \qquad (4\text{-}22)$$

---

[5] The relativistic formula (14), or (18), thus replaces the classical formula (9′), where $\delta m = 0$.

Taking account of (2-67) we obtain, in full accord with (15),

$$F^i \, d\tau = m_0 \, dV^i, \qquad (4\text{-}23)$$

where m_0 represents the *proper mass*, or *rest mass*, of the particle (a conserved scalar under the present hypotheses), F^i is the space-time four-vector of force (necessarily orthogonal to V^i under these hypotheses[6]), and $d\tau$ is the element of the proper time.

The finite force F^i is thus defined in a way specially related to (2-64), and this is possible only when there exists a four-velocity field. In the general procedure, on the contrary, one is led to link the force density f^i to an integral tensor F^{ij} of rank 2, and to write formula (23) in the form

$$F^{ij} \, dx_j = dp^i, \qquad (4\text{-}24)$$

with

$$p^i = m_0 V^i \qquad (4\text{-}25)$$

and, of course, in view of (2-40),

$$p_i p^i = - c^2 m_0{}^2 = \text{const}. \qquad (4\text{-}26)$$

The relation between the two preceding definitions of the finite force is clearly

$$F^i = F^{ij} V_j, \qquad (4\text{-}27)$$

and the necessary and sufficient condition that m_0 be constant is that the tensor F^{ij} be antisymmetric, as in the electromagnetic case ($F^{ij} = Q H^{ij}$). If F^{ij} is a field quantity defined independently of the velocity V_j of the particle, Eq. (27) shows that the four-vector F^i will nevertheless depend on the velocity. Thus the covariant definition of the force, in finite form, as an antisymmetric tensor of rank 2 is more intrinsic than its definition as a four-vector.

The *Maupertuisian* or *relative mass* m of the particle, varying

---

[6] It is directed along the principal normal of the space-time trajectory.

with the velocity, is by definition such that[7]

$$p^u = mv^u \quad \text{and} \quad p^4 = icm. \quad (4\text{-}28)$$

Its relation to the rest mass is thus

$$m = \frac{m_0}{\sqrt{1 - \beta^2}}. \quad (4\text{-}29)$$

The expressions (28) clearly justify the name momentum-energy given to the four-vector (25).

By (29), the series expansion of the energy W associated with the Maupertuisian mass m is

$$W = c^2 m = m_0 c^2 + \tfrac{1}{2} m_0 v^2 + \cdots. \quad (4\text{-}30)$$

To the *dormant energy* $c^2 m_0$ associated with the rest mass m_0 there is thus added the *lively* or *kinetic energy* $\tfrac{1}{2} m_0 v^2 + \cdots$, whose value is purely *relative*. In classical mechanics it was awkward to try to explain how the obviously *relative* character of the kinetic energy was in accord with the reputedly *absolute* character of energy in general. This difficulty disappears in relativistic mechanics, since there all Maupertuisian energy has the variability of the fourth component of a four-vector.

From (29) we obtain

$$dm = m_0 (1 - \beta^2)^{-3/2} \boldsymbol{\beta} \cdot d\boldsymbol{\beta} = m(1 - \beta^2)^{-1} \boldsymbol{\beta} \cdot d\boldsymbol{\beta}, \quad (4\text{-}31)$$

which implies a corrective factor to the classical formula

$$dW = m\boldsymbol{v} \cdot d\boldsymbol{v}.$$

Again, we have

$$d(m\,\boldsymbol{v}) = m\,d\boldsymbol{v} + \boldsymbol{v}\,dm. \quad (4\text{-}32)$$

From (31) and (32) we deduce, in the special cases of transverse

---

[7] It is the quantity defined in footnote 4.

and longitudinal acceleration, respectively,

$$d(m\boldsymbol{v}) = m\,d\boldsymbol{v} \quad \text{if} \quad \boldsymbol{v}\cdot d\boldsymbol{v} = 0,$$
$$d(m\boldsymbol{v}) = m\frac{d\boldsymbol{v}}{1-\beta^2} \quad \text{if} \quad \boldsymbol{v}\times d\boldsymbol{v} = 0. \tag{4-33}$$

Abelé and Malvaux[8] point out that in the longitudinal case

$$Dv = \frac{dv}{1-\beta^2} \tag{4-34}$$

is precisely the infinitesimal velocity that must be *combined according to* (2-30) with the initial velocity to obtain the final velocity.

Formulas (33) and (34), where m denotes the Maupertuisian mass defined in (28), are the relativistic generalizations of the classical formula $d(m\boldsymbol{v}) = m\,d\boldsymbol{v}$.

4.6   Relativistic Impact of Two Identical Particles, One of Which Is Initially at Rest

The incident particle strikes an identical particle initially at rest at a point A of ordinary space. Let θ be the angle, in ordinary space, between the directions of the velocities of the two particles after impact. It is left as an exercise for the reader to show, by means of the laws of conservation of momentum and energy, that

$$\cos\theta = \left(\frac{(m_2 - m_0)}{(m_2 + m_0)}\frac{(m_3 - m_0)}{(m_3 + m_0)}\right)^{\frac{1}{2}}, \tag{4-35}$$

where m_2 and m_3 denote the Maupertuisian masses of the two particles after impact, their rest masses both being m_0.

The angle θ is acute, and it is smaller the faster the incident particle. For a slow-moving incident particle, $m_2 \approx m_0$, $m_3 \approx m_0$, $\theta \approx \pi/2$ (as in classical mechanics).

[8] "Vitesse et Univers Relativiste." S.E.D.E.S., Paris, 1954.

The validity of this formula has been well verified by photographs of impacts of particles taken in Wilson cloud chambers.

We note that the formula is the same no matter which of the emerging particles was the one initially at rest. This is compatible with the principle of the indistinguishability of quantum particles.

B.   Further Developments

4.7   Sources or Sinks of Energy or Mass

Let us assume that formula (7), with T^{ij} given by (11), remains true if we give up the condition (5) or (10) that was used in deriving it.

On retracing the calculation that led to (14) and (18) we find this time that

$$\partial_j (\rho_0 V^j) = - c^{-2} V_i f^i , \qquad (4\text{-}36)$$

or, in integral form,

$$c^2 \iiint\limits_{\mathscr{C}_2 - \mathscr{C}_1} \rho_0 \, \delta u_0 = - \iiint V_i f^i \, d\omega \qquad (4\text{-}37)$$

which has the same form as Eq. (3-56), which refers to the case of Joule heat.

The density $V_i f^i$ is thus a density of sources or sinks of kinetic energy (in the case of Joule heat) or of masslike energy (in the case of hydrodynamic sources or sinks).

4.8   Work Done by Surface Forces

We shall illustrate the phenomenon in the simplest case, that of an isotropic pressure.

The classical formula for the surface force of pressure,

$$\delta F = \varpi \, \delta s \tag{4-38}$$

has as its obvious relativistic extension

$$\delta F^{ij} = \varpi \, \delta s^{ij}, \tag{4-39}$$

where δs^{ij} denotes the tensorial surface element defined in (2-70).

Consider the fluid tube with lateral wall $\mathscr{W}$ generated in space-time by a material droplet followed in its motion. The work of the pressure is evidently

$$\iint\limits_{\mathscr{W}}\int \delta F^{ij} \, dx_j \equiv \iint\limits_{\mathscr{W}}\int \varpi \, \delta s^{ij} \, dx_j \equiv \iint\limits_{\mathscr{W}}\int \varpi \, du^i$$

$$= \iint\int\int \partial^i \varpi \, d\omega - \iint\limits_{\mathscr{C}_2 - \mathscr{C}_1}\int \varpi \, du^i,$$

where, as usual, we have denoted by $\mathscr{C}_1$ and $\mathscr{C}_2$ the boundary hypercuts, and by du^i the four-vector element of volume.

If the tube is extremely slender, we can take $\mathscr{C}_1$ and $\mathscr{C}_2$ orthogonal to the four-velocity V^i. Formula (2-64) then allows us to write

$$du^i = -c^{-2} \, du_0 \, V^i = -c^{-2} V^i V^j \, du_j. \tag{4-40}$$

Taking account of the fact that $V^j \, du_j = 0$, we have

$$-c^{-2} \iint\int\int \partial_j(\varpi V^i V^j) \, d\omega = \iint\limits_{\mathscr{C}_2 - \mathscr{C}_1}\int \varpi \, du^i,$$

and the expression for the work done by the pressure becomes

$$\iint\int\int \{ \partial^i \varpi + c^{-2} \, \partial_j(\varpi V^i V^j) \} \, d\omega.$$

If, then, in addition to $\partial^i \varpi$ the fluid is under the influence of a volume force density f^i with T^{ij} given by (11), we find, on taking account of (16), the equation of motion

$$f^i - \partial^i \varpi = \partial_j \{ (\rho_0 - c^{-2}\varpi) \, V^i V^j \}. \tag{4-41}$$

Incidentally, we have here once again come upon the well-known equivalence between a pressure and a proper energy density.

Forgetting the inductive process utilized in obtaining it, we assume that formula (41) has general validity.

If, with (41) and under the hypothesis (10), we retrace the calculation that led to (14), we find that

$$\partial_i(\rho_0 V^i) = c^{-2}\varpi\, \partial_i V^i \tag{4-42}$$

and, instead of (18),

$$c^2 \iint\limits_{\mathscr{C}_2 - \mathscr{C}_1}\int \rho_0\, \delta u_0 = \iiint\int \varpi\, \partial_i V^i\, d\omega, \tag{4-43}$$

this being the covariant generalization of the classical formula

$$dW = \int \varpi\, du \qquad (\text{cf. (2-66) and (2-67)}).$$

4.9   The Angular Momentum-Barycentric Moment Tensor

If we denote the momentum-energy of a particle, as usual, by p^i, the *space-time angular momentum* of this point relative to an arbitrary space-time origin will be, by definition,

$$S^{ij} = x^i p^j - x^j p^i. \tag{4-44}$$

The three components with superscripts 23, 31, and 12 evidently represent the angular momentum in the classical sense. Let us seek the interpretation of the three other components ($u = 1, 2, 3$)

$$S^{u4} = x^u p^4 - x^4 p^u = \mathrm{i}c(mx^u - v^u t), \tag{4-45}$$

the latter form following from (2-3) and (4-28). For $t = 0$, they are $\mathrm{i}c$ times the barycentric moment mx, which is the vector that enters the classical definition of the barycenter, or center of mass. For $t = dt$, there appears in addition the correction for non-simultaneity $-v\, dt$ whose interpretation is obvious.

In the general case, we say that the *space-time angular momentum* tensor S^{ij} represents the *angular momentum-barycentric moment* of the particle.

4.10   Barycenter, and Moment about the Barycenter, of a Cloud of Particles [9]

Consider a cloud of particles with momentum-energies p^i and point-instants x^i. By definition the total momentum-energy will be

$$P^i = \sum p^i. \tag{4-46}$$

Since the p^i are timelike with their fourth components always positive (apart from the factor ic—cf. Eq. (4-25)), the same will be true of P^i.

We postulate as the definition of the *total mass* of the cloud

$$P^4 = icM. \tag{4-47}$$

As in the classical theory of vectors, we say that the system of sliding vectors p^i constitutes a *wrench* with resultant P^i. Let us seek the *axis* of this *wrench* and the *resultant moment* S^{ij} about the axis.

It is natural to introduce the equation

$$X^i P^j - X^j P^i + S^{ij} = \sum \left[x^i p^j - x^j p^i \right], \tag{4-48}$$

which represents six linear equations for the $4 + 6 = 10$ unknowns p^i and S^{ij}. Four supplementary linear equations are now, in principle, necessary, and it is natural to take

$$S^{ij} P_j = 0. \tag{4-49}$$

The system (48) and (49) is solved very easily in the proper frame $\mathscr{L}_0$ of the vector P^i, which, by definition, is such that

---

[9] This definition was given independently by Papapetrou, Pryce, Møller, Fokker, and ourselves.

$P_{(0)}^u = 0$. In this frame we have from (49) and then from (48),

$$S_{(0)}^{u4} = 0, \qquad S_{(0)}^{uv} = \sum \left[x^u p^v - x^v p^u \right], \qquad (4\text{-}50)$$

$$MX_{(0)}^u = \sum \left[mx^u - v^u t \right]. \qquad (4\text{-}51)$$

Of the 10 unknowns $X_{(0)}^i$ and $S_{(0)}^{ij}$, only $X_{(0)}^4$ remains arbitrary. This stems from the fact that of the 4 equations (49), only 3 are independent (since $S^{ij} P_j P_i \equiv 0$).

The formulas (50) and (51) completely define the (timelike) *axis* of the *wrench* by means of the 3 coordinates $X_{(0)}^u$ of its spatial trace and the 6 components $S_{(0)}^{ij}$ of the central *resultant moment*. From the dynamical point of view, the three $X_{(0)}^u$ are the coordinates of the *barycenter* of the cloud (at rest in the proper frame of the total momentum-energy), and the three $S_{(0)}^{uv}$ are its *angular momentum about the barycenter*.

4.11   The Problem of the Proper or Spin Angular Momentum: Case of Continuous Media

We know that reasons connected with atomic spectra led Uhlenbeck and Goudsmit in 1925 to attribute to the electron a proper angular momentum and a proper magnetic moment. But Dirac's relativistic quantum theory of the electron of 1927 contains intrinsically in its formalism, among other marvels, precisely what is necessary to endow the electron with a proper angular momentum and a proper magnetic moment, with precisely the values postulated by Uhlenbeck and Goudsmit on the basis of experiment.

As a relativistic extension of the Schrödinger equation, the Dirac equation defines a whole collection of physical densities expressed in tensor form. In particular it represents the proper angular momentum density by a completely antisymmetric tensor of the third rank, σ^{ijk}, and the magnetic and electric moment densities by an antisymmetric tensor M^{ij} of the second rank, as was necessary. Moreover, the canonical momentum-energy tensor T^{ij} that appears in its formalism is asymmetric and satisfies the Tetrode equation

$$T^{ij} - T^{ji} + \partial_k \, \partial^{ijk} = 0 \, . \qquad (4\text{-}52)$$

We shall now show that once we assume the necessity of defining a *proper* angular momentum density, quite general arguments allow us to justify *a priori* most of the above points and to perceive some interesting consequences.

The need to define the spin density as a tensor of the third rank antisymmetric in at least the first two indices, σ^{ijk}, can be seen from the formula giving the orbital angular momentum of a continuous medium without spin (described by a symmetric momentum-energy tensor T^{ij}), namely

$$x^i p^j - x^j p^i = \int \int \int (x^i T^{jk} - x^j T^{ik}) \, du_k \, , \qquad (4\text{-}53)$$

since the quantity in parentheses, which represents the orbital angular momentum density, is a tensor of the third rank that is antisymmetric in the indices i and j. Thus if Physics imposes the idea of endowing particles with a proper angular momentum, this quantity has to be represented by an antisymmetric tensor of the second rank s^{ij} related to the corresponding density σ by the formula

$$s^{ij} = \int \int \int \sigma^{ijk} \, du_k \, . \qquad (4\text{-}54)$$

Let us now try to understand the Tetrode formula (52) and the fact that the Dirac σ^{ijk} is completely antisymmetric.

As we know, in the classical theory of elasticity the necessary and sufficient condition that the elastic tensor E^{uv} ($u, v, w = 1, 2, 3$) be asymmetric is that there exist a ponderomotive torque density μ^{uv}. To be more specific, the orbital ponderomotive torque

$$\int \int \int (x^u f^v - x^v f^u) \, du$$

generated by the elastic force density

$$f^u = \partial_v E^{uv}$$

must balance the proper ponderomotive couple

$$- \int \int \int \mu^{uv} \, du \, .$$

Therefore

$$\int \int \int \left(x^u \, \partial_w E^{vw} - x^v \, \partial_w E^{uv} + \mu^{uv} \right) du = 0 \, ,$$

whence, on noting that $\partial_w x^u \equiv \delta_w^u$ and that

$$x^u \, \partial_w E^{vw} = \partial_w \left(x^u E^{vw} \right) - E^{vu} \, ,$$

we have

$$\int \int \int \left(E^{uv} - E^{vu} + \mu^{uv} \right) du = 0$$

(since the double integral

$$\int \int \left(x^u E^{vw} - x^v E^{uw} \right) ds_w$$

taken over a contour exterior to the body is zero). We conclude that in the classical theory of elasticity, when the ponderomotive torque density μ^{uv} is present, the elastic tensor is not symmetric but obeys the equation

$$E^{uv} - E^{vu} + \mu^{uv} = 0 \, . \tag{4-55}$$

The similarity of formulas (52) and (55) becomes total if we introduce, in a formal way, a torque density μ^{ij} associated with the spin density σ^{ijk} by the formula

$$\mu^{ij}_{\smile} = \partial_k \sigma^{ijk}_{\smile} \tag{4-56}$$

completely analogous to (7).

In deriving (52) we obtain

$$\partial_j \left(T^{ij} - T^{ji} \right) + \partial_{kj} \sigma^{ijk} = 0 \tag{4-57}$$

and since the tensor $\partial_{kj} = \partial_j \, \partial_k$ is essentially symmetric (in *flat* space-time) we see that, apart from the rather special case

$\partial_{jk}\sigma^{ijk} \equiv 0$, the condition for

$$\partial_j T^{ij} = \partial_j T^{ji} \tag{4-58}$$

to be valid is that the tensor σ^{ijk} (already antisymmetric in ij) be completely antisymmetric.

The total angular momentum of a medium endowed with spin is thus

$$x^i P^j - x^j P^i + S^{ij}_{\smile} = \int \int \int (x^i T^{jk} - x^j T^{ik} + \sigma^{ijk}_{\smile}) \, du_k \tag{4-59}$$

with an asymmetric T^{ij} and, if we require (52) and (58), a completely antisymmetric σ^{ijk}. Taking the integral over a closed hypersurface $\mathscr{C}_2 - \mathscr{C}_1 + \mathscr{W}$ of the usual type, and taking account of the definition (7) and the Tetrode formula (52), we obtain

$$\int \int \int \int (x^i f^j - x^j f^i) \, d\omega = \int\!\!\!\int\!\!\!\int_{\mathscr{C}_2 - \mathscr{C}_1} (x^i T^{jk} - x^j T^{ik} + \sigma^{ijk}) \, du_k. \tag{4-60}$$

Thus the Dirac σ^{ijk} does *not* yield the inertial response of the electron to the electromagnetic ponderomotive torque (3-81). It belongs to internal degrees of freedom that respond, as does the momentum-energy tensor T^{ij}, to the "orbital" torque created by the Lorentz force density (3-33). We note incidentally, that E. Durand[10] has extracted from the Dirac theory an expression for a different spin density, σ^{*ijk}, antisymmetric in ij only, which obeys formula (56) with the μ^{ij} given by the electromagnetic expression (3-81) and (3-72) [or (3-82) and (3-83)].

Using (52), we can rewrite (60) as

$$\int \int \int \int (x^i f^j - x^j f^i) \, d\omega$$
$$= \int\!\!\!\int\!\!\!\int_{\mathscr{C}_2 - \mathscr{C}_1} (x^i T^{jk}_{\underline{}} - x^j T^{ik}_{\underline{}}) \, du_k, \tag{4-61}$$

where $T^{ij}_{\underline{}}$ denotes, of course, the symmetric part of T^{ij}. Most authors conclude from this that the true momentum-energy

[10] *Compt. Rend.* **218**, 36, 961 (1944).

tensor of the Dirac electron is not the asymmetric T^{ij} deduced from the canonical formalism but the symmetrized tensor $T^{ij}_{\underline{\ }}$. However, one can adduce arguments leading to the contrary conclusion that the asymmetric tensor T^{ij} is the preferable momentum-energy tensor of the Dirac electron.

The first argument, somewhat formal, is that it is the triple integral (60) and not the triple integral (61) that transfers into tensorial form the operational expression of the angular momentum first integrals. The second argument is that the Dirac theory contains two electric current densities linked to each other by a relation of the classical electromagnetic type (3-66) and (3-67)

$$j^k = j^k_{(m)} + \partial_l M^{kl}. \tag{4-62}$$

It is possible to establish a very close parallel between formulas (52) and (62) of the Dirac theory. From this one can show that consequences of the noncollinearity of j^k and $j^k_{(m)}$ that are in principle observable and are deducible equally well from the Dirac electron theory and the Maxwell photon theory,[11] have a direct interpretation in terms of the asymmetric tensor T^{ij} (and only an indirect interpretation in terms of the symmetrized tensor T^{ij}).

4.12 The Problem of the Proper or Spin Angular Momentum: Weyssenhof's Theory

Consider a fluid endowed with spin conforming to the pre-

---

[11] See our articles on the "inertial effect of spin" of the moving electron and photon, *Phys. Rev.* **134,** B 471 (1964); and **139,** B 1443 (1965). See also *Ann. Inst. Henri-Poincaré* **IIA,** 131 (1965) and *Cahiers Phys.* **18,** 471 (1965).

General arguments in favor of the use of a nonsymmetric T^{ij} in media endowed with spin were given by ourselves, *J. Math.* **22,** 118 (1943); by Weyssenhof, *Acta Phys. Polon.* **9,** 7 and 26 (1947); by Papapetrou, *Phil. Mag.* **40,** 937 (1949) and *Proc. Roy. Soc., London* **A209,** 248 (1951); and by Sciama, *Proc. Cambridge Phil. Soc.* **54,** 72 (1958).

ceding scheme, but with the tensors T^{ij} and σ^{ijk} having the particular forms

$$T^{ij} = g^i V^j, \qquad \sigma^{ijk}_{\smile} = g^{ij}_{\smile} V^k, \tag{4-63}$$

where V^j denotes the kinematic four-velocity. Taking a closed three-dimensional bounding hypersurface $\mathscr{C}_2 - \mathscr{C}_1 + \mathscr{W}$ of the type in Fig. 10, and noting as usual that $\delta u_0 = V^i\, du_i$ is zero on $\mathscr{W}$, we obtain

$$\iiint_{\mathscr{C}_2 - \mathscr{C}_1} T^{ij}\, du_j \equiv \iiint_{\mathscr{C}_2 - \mathscr{C}_1} g^i\, du_0 = \iiiint \partial_j T^{ij}\, d\omega, \tag{4-64}$$

$$\iiint_{\mathscr{C}_2 - \mathscr{C}_1} (x^i T^{jk} - x^j T^{ik} + \sigma^{ijk}_{\smile})\, du_k$$

$$\equiv \iiint_{\mathscr{C}_2 - \mathscr{C}_1} (x^i g^j - x^j g^i + g^{ij}_{\smile})\, du_0$$

$$= \iiiint (T^{ij} - T^{ji} + \partial_k \sigma^{ijk})\, d\omega. \tag{4-65}$$

If we postulate the validity of the Tetrode formula (52), these expressions vanish when there are no external forces or torques.

With Frenkel[12] and Mathisson,[13] Weyssenhof[14] takes as his additional condition

$$g^{ij}_{\smile} V_j = 0. \tag{4-66}$$

One goes from the case of a fluid to that of a particle by shrinking a fluid filament to negligible thickness, as in §5. Writing

$$p^i = \lim \iiint g^i\, du_0, \qquad s^{ij}_{\smile} = \lim \iiint g^{ij}_{\smile}\, du_0, \tag{4-67}$$

and including, this time, a ponderomotive force F^{ij} and a

[12] Z. Physik **37**, 243 (1926).

[13] Z. Physik **67**, 270 and 826 (1931); Math. Ann. **107**, 400 (1933); Acta Phys. Polon. **6**, 163 and 218 (1937).

[14] Acta Phys. Polon. **9**, 7 and 26 (1947).

ponderomotive torque M^{ijk}, we find the following equations of motion (in which the derivatives are taken with respect to the proper time):

$$F^i \equiv F^{ij}V_j = p'^i \qquad (4\text{-}68)$$

$$M^{ij}_{\smile} \equiv M^{ijk}_{\smile}V_k = x^j p'^i - x^j p'^i + x'^i p^j - x'^j p^i + g'^{ij}_{\smile} \qquad (4\text{-}69)$$

or

$$M^{ij}_{\smile} \equiv M^{ijk}_{\smile}V_k = x'^i p^j - x'^j p^i + s'^{ij}_{\smile}. \qquad (4\text{-}70)$$

If the tensor F^{ij} contains a nonvanishing symmetric part, the length of the momentum-energy changes. As for condition (66), it becomes

$$s^{ij}_{\smile}V_j = 0, \qquad (4\text{-}71)$$

which thus differs from our relation (49).

It is interesting to note that equations (69) and (70) are *formally* identical with those of the *statics* of stiff filaments:

$$d\boldsymbol{t} = \boldsymbol{f}\,dl, \qquad d\boldsymbol{l} \times \boldsymbol{t} + d\boldsymbol{\gamma} = \boldsymbol{\mu}\,dl,$$

where $\boldsymbol{f}$ and $\boldsymbol{\mu}$ denote linear densities of the applied force and torque, and $\boldsymbol{t}$ and $\boldsymbol{\gamma}$ denote the tension and stiffness of the filament. The complete table of this correspondence is shown in Table I.

TABLE I

CORRESPONDENCE BETWEEN THE CLASSICAL STATICS OF SYSTEMS OF
FILAMENTS AND THE RELATIVISTIC DYNAMICS OF SYSTEMS OF PARTICLES

Classical statics of systems of filaments	Relativistic dynamics of systems of particles
Filaments in Euclidean space	Trajectories in Minkowskian space-time
Tensions of the filaments	Momentum-energies of the particles
Linear density of applied force	Force = linear density of applied momentum-energy
Rigidity of filaments	"Spins" of the particles
Linear density of applied torque	Ponderomotive moment = linear density of applied spin

4.13   General Theorems of the Dynamics of Systems of Particles

Let us now introduce the *interactions* between the particles x^i, p^i. As in the case of an electromagnetic field (cf. §§3.5 and 3.6) we shall have to assume that a *potential momentum-energy*, represented by a tensor T^{ij}, is distributed throughout the field according to a particular law. It can be shown, however, that it is also necessary to introduce a *density of potential angular momentum*, represented by a tensor σ^{ijk} of rank 3 that is necessarily antisymmetric with respect to the first two indices—a tensor that in fact exists in the electromagnetic field and in most of the other physical fields ("fields endowed with spin" of the quantized theory).

The equations of §4.10 must therefore be completed so as to read

$$P^i = \sum p^i + \int \int \int T^{ij}\, \delta u_i = \text{const}, \qquad (4\text{-}72)$$

$$X^i P^j - X^j P^i + S^{ij}$$

$$+ \int \int \int [x^i T^{jk} - x^j T^{ik} + \sigma^{ijk}]\, \delta u_k = \text{const}. \qquad (4\text{-}73)$$

For $i = u = 1, 2, 3$, Eqs. (72) express, in relativistic form, the theorem of the conservation of total momentum, and for $i = 4$ both the theorem of the conservation of total mass and the kinetic energy theorem.[15]

As for Eqs. (73), for $i, j = u, v = 1, 2, 3$, they express the theorem of the conservation of total angular momentum and, for $i, j = u$, 4, the theorem of the barycenter. The barycenter of the system

---

[15] The total mass is less than the sum of the Maupertuisian masses of the particles of the cloud, because it contains also the mass equivalent of the potential energy, which is negative in a stable case. This is the *mass defect* associated with the *binding energy*, very well observed in particle physics, and is a direct consequence of the law of the equivalence of mass and energy.

(particles + field) moves with uniform speed in a straight line collinear with the total momentum-energy.

Contrary to the situation in Newtonian mechanics, the *general theorems* can not be used as intermediaries in the solution of problems. This is because in relativity we have to solve as a single whole the double problem of the motion of the points and the propagation of the waves of interaction that transport the momentum-energy and the angular momentum with a finite velocity.

Chapter 5

ANALYTICAL DYNAMICS

A. Dynamics of a Charged Particle

5.1 Elements of Relativistic Analytical Mechanics of the Electrically Charged Particle

We return to formulas (3-39) and (3-40), which we here rewrite:

$$dP^i = - Q \, \partial^i A^j \, dx_j, \qquad (5\text{-}1)$$

$$P^i = p^i - QA^i, \qquad (5\text{-}2)$$

where p^i, as always, denotes the kinetic or proper momentum-energy of the particle of charge Q, $-QA^i$ denotes its potential momentum-energy of electromagnetic origin (A^i being the four-potential), and P^i denotes the combined momentum-energy.

In analytical mechanics we assume that the trajectory actually described belongs to a congruence of virtual trajectories. Because of this, if dx_j denotes the element of space-time trajectory, the expression $\partial^i p^j \, dx_j$ has meaning. Moreover it is zero if p^j has constant length, which is actually the case. On adding it to the second term of (1) we obtain

$$[\partial^j P^i - \partial^i P^j] \, dx_j = 0. \qquad (5\text{-}3)$$

A particularly important case is that in which the four-potential A^i remains constant in magnitude and direction along the parallel lines of a pencil, which we shall take to be parallel to one of the axes, say x^i:

$$\partial^i A^j = 0 \qquad \text{for given } i . \tag{5-4}$$

It then follows from (1) that along these lines

$$P^i = p^i - QA^i = \text{const} \tag{5-5}$$

and we say that the component P^i of the combined momentum-energy is a *first integral*.

The most important case in actual practice is that in which $i = 4$. Here we have

$$W = c^2 QV + \text{const} \tag{5-6}$$

with, of course (cf. (3-7)),

$$\begin{aligned} V &= - iA^4, \\ W &= - icp^4 = m_0 (c^2 + \tfrac{1}{2}v^2 + \cdots). \end{aligned} \tag{5-7}$$

From formula (3) we can deduce quite a collection of elegant formulas involving simple or double integrals having the dimensions of action. The most important of these formulas is the one that expresses the *Hamilton–Jacobi theorem*, since it leads directly to the geometrical approximation of wave mechanics.

If δx_i is a spacelike four-displacement, we conclude from (3) that

$$\left[\partial^j P^i - \partial^i P^j\right] \delta x_i \, dx_j \equiv dP^i \, \delta x_i - \delta P^i \, dx_i = 0 , \tag{5-8}$$

where we have written

$$dP^i = \partial^j P^i \, dx_j, \qquad \delta P^j = \partial^i P^j \, \delta x_i . \tag{5-9}$$

This elegant dynamical invariant form was given by Poincaré and, in relativistic language, by E. Cartan.[1]

---

[1] "Leçons sur les Invariants Intégraux." Hermann, Paris, 1922.

Conversely, since the δx_i are arbitrary, (8) implies (3) or (1).

Integrate (3) along a trajectory $\mathscr{T}$ between two point-instants K_1 and K_2:

$$P^i_{(2)} - P^i_{(1)} = \int\limits_{K_1 K_2} \partial^i P^j \, dx_j. \qquad (5\text{-}10)$$

Now with each point of $\mathscr{T}$ associate a spacelike four-displacement δx_i, a function of x_j, and assume that each contour $\int \delta x_i$, or $\mathscr{F}$, is closed. Then we see from (10) that

$$\oint\limits_2 P^i \, \delta x_i - \oint\limits_1 P^i \, \delta x_i = \int\limits_{\mathscr{T}} dx_j \oint\limits_{\mathscr{F}} \partial^i P^j \, \delta x_i = 0,$$

the symbol δ referring to a change of trajectory $\mathscr{T}$. From this we obtain:

THEOREM.   *The line integral of the combined action taken around a closed spacelike curve moving with the fluid is conserved:*

$$\mathscr{A} \equiv \oint\limits_{\mathscr{F}} P^i \, \delta x_i = \text{const}. \qquad (5\text{-}11)$$

COROLLARY.   *The flux of the curl of the momentum-energy across a two-dimensional cap $\mathscr{S}$ moving with the fluid is conserved:*

$$\mathscr{A} \equiv \tfrac{1}{2} \int\!\!\int\limits_{\mathscr{S}} (\partial^i P^j - \partial^j P^i)[dx_i \, dx_j] = \text{const}. \qquad (5\text{-}12)$$

From (12), or from (8), we conclude that

$$\int\!\!\int\limits_{\mathscr{S}} (\delta_1 P^i \, \delta_2 x_i - \delta_2 P^i \, \delta_1 x_i) = 0. \qquad (5\text{-}13)$$

To return from (12) or (13) to (3) it suffices to take the integral over a closed two-dimensional surface and to note that the transformed triple integral is identically zero.

5.2 The Hamilton–Jacobi Theorem

Let us calculate the *variation of the combined action along a space-time trajectory* between two fixed point-instants K_1 and K_2 with coordinates $x^i_{(1)}$ and $x^i_{(2)}$. We obtain, in the usual way,

$$\delta \int_{K_1 K_2} P^i \, dx_i = \int_{K_1 K_2} \delta P^i \, dx_i + \int_{K_1 K_2} P^i \, d \, \delta x_i$$

$$= \left[P^i \, \delta x_i \right]_{x^i_{(1)}}^{x^i_{(2)}} + \int_{K_1 K_2} \{ \delta P^i \, dx_i - dP^i \, \delta x_i \}. \qquad (5\text{-}14)$$

Since, by hypothesis, the points K_1 and K_2 are fixed,

$$\delta x_{i(2)} = \delta x_{i(1)} = 0.$$

The necessary and sufficient condition that (8) or (3) or (1) hold, i.e., that the equations of motion (4-24) be satisfied with (3-38), is thus that

$$\delta \mathscr{A} = \delta \int_{K_1 K_2} P^i \, dx_i = 0, \qquad (5\text{-}15)$$

always with (2). From this follows:

THE HAMILTON–JACOBI THEOREM. *The combined action is stationary along an actual trajectory.*

Now suppose that the $\delta x_{i(1)}$ and $\delta x_{i(2)}$ are no longer zero. It follows from the preceding calculation that, if (15) holds, the validity of either one of

$$(P^i \, \delta x_i)_{K_1} = 0, \qquad (P^i \, \delta x_i)_{K_2} = 0 \qquad (5\text{-}16)$$

implies that of the other. Hence we have:

COROLLARY.   *If the congruence of the lines of momentum-energy*[2]
*admits a hypersurface orthogonal trajectory, it admits an infinite
number of them* (*Hamilton–Jacobi surfaces or wave surfaces* Σ).

With this hypothesis, and without changing anything intrinsic, we can take

$$\mathscr{A} = \text{constant on } \Sigma . \tag{5-17}$$

It then follows from the above that

$$\partial^i \mathscr{A} = P^i \equiv p^i - QA^i , \tag{5-18}$$

whence, by (4-26), we conclude that

$$(\partial^i \mathscr{A} + QA^i)(\partial_i \mathscr{A} + QA_i) = - c^2 m_0{}^2 . \tag{5-19}$$

This partial differential equation of the first order and the
second degree is the relativistic form of the fundamental
equation of geometrical optics.

5.3   The Lagrange Equations

If the P^i and the x_i are expressed as functions of a single
parameter θ, the element of action can be written

$$d\mathscr{A} \equiv P^i x_i' \, d\theta = \mathscr{L}(\theta) \, d\theta , \tag{5-20}$$

the *Lagrangian function* being

$$\mathscr{L} = P^i x_i' , \qquad x_i' \equiv \frac{dx_i}{d\theta}. \tag{5-21}$$

It is customary to consider $\mathscr{L}$ to be a function of θ, which
enters through the x_i and the x_i'. If we denote the corresponding

---

[2] Beware! The lines of combined momentum-energy do not coincide with
the space-time trajectories! They are not even necessarily timelike.

partial derivatives by $\partial^i \mathscr{L}$ and $\partial'^i \mathscr{L}$, we find in the standard way (taking account of the Hamilton–Jacobi theorem) that

$$\delta \int_{K_1 K_2} \mathscr{L} \, d\theta = \int_{K_1 K_2} (\partial^i \mathscr{L} \, \delta x_i + \partial'^i \mathscr{L} \, \delta x'^i) \, d\theta$$

$$= \int_{K_1 K_2} (\partial^i \mathscr{L} \, \delta x_i \, d\theta + \partial'^i \mathscr{L} \, d \, \delta x_i)$$

$$= \left[\partial'^i \mathscr{L} \, \delta x_i \right]_{K_1}^{K_2} + \int_{K_1 K_2} \left[\partial^i \mathscr{L} - \frac{d}{d\theta} (\partial'^i \mathscr{L}) \right] \delta x_i \, d\theta = 0 \,,$$

whence we obtain the Lagrange equations

$$\frac{d}{d\theta} \frac{\partial \mathscr{L}}{\partial x_i'} = \frac{\partial \mathscr{L}}{\partial x_i} \,, \tag{5-22}$$

which are actually covariant in form.

5.4 Compatibility of Relativistic Analytical Mechanics and the Old Quantum Theory

In the old quantum theory the action integrals

$$\int_{\mathscr{T}} P^i \, dx_i \,, \qquad \oint_{\mathscr{F}} P^i \, \delta x_i \,, \qquad \iint (\delta_1 P^i \, \delta_2 x_i - \delta_2 P^i \, \delta_1 x_i)$$

were required to be equal to integral multiples of Planck's constant h. The manifest Minkowski covariance of the above expressions shows the inherent compatibility of the two theories.

B. Dynamics of a System of Charged Particles. The Wheeler–Feynman Theory [3]

5.5 General Postulates

a. No Self-Interaction of Point Charges Q. This approximation, which is certainly unjustified at the quantum level, is acceptable at the macroscopic level where, for example, we can incorporate the self-mass (assumed constant) as part of the observed mass. This hypothesis is self-consistent only if the interaction moves with the limiting velocity c, i.e., if the mass of the photon is zero, or negligible, since otherwise the trajectories of the photons could intersect those of the point charges a second time.

b. Every Photon Emitted in the System is Absorbed in the System. By this postulate we separate the problem of the *interaction* of the charges from that of their *radiation* (which will be treated separately). The *interaction*, by definition, will be a process that is completely symmetric between past and future (as in the conservative systems of Newtonian mechanics). It will thus be naturally described by means of semiadvanced and semiretarded waves. In the language of quantum field theory, the Wheeler–Feynman theory is concerned only with the "virtual photons," these being precisely the ones that carry the interaction.

[3] Wheeler and Feynman, *Rev. Modern Phys.* **17**, 157 (1945); **21**, 425 (1949). See also Schwarzschild, *Gött. Nachr.* **128**, 132 (1903); Tetrode, *Z. Physik* **10**, 317 (1922); Frenkel, *ibid.* **32**, 518 (1925); Fokker, *ibid.* **58**, 386 (1929); *Physica* **9**, 33 (1929); **12**, 145 (1932); Dirac, *Proc. Roy. Soc.* (London) **A167**, 148 (1938); Van Dam and Wigner, *Phys. Rev.* **138**, B 1576 (1965).

5.6   Currents and Potentials

Let $\mathscr{T}_a$ be the space-time trajectory of a point charge Q_a passing through the point-instant a^i, and let α be a parameter that increases monotonically along $\mathscr{T}_a$ from $-\infty$ to $+\infty$ in the same sense as the time. Denoting by δ the singular Dirac function, we introduce, with Dirac, the current density[4]

$$j^i = Q_a \int_{-\infty}^{+\infty} \delta(x-a)\, da^i$$

$$\equiv (2\pi)^{-4} Q_a \int_{-\infty}^{+\infty} da^i \int\!\!\int\!\!\int\!\!\int_{-\infty}^{+\infty}$$

$$\times \exp[ik^j(x-a)_j]\, dk^1\, dk^2\, dk^3\, dk^4/i, \qquad (5\text{-}23)$$

and the potential

$$A^i = -\frac{1}{4\pi} Q_a \int_{\alpha=-\infty}^{\alpha=+\infty} \delta(r^2)\, da^i \qquad (5\text{-}24)$$

created by Q_a, where

$$r^i = x^i - a^i, \qquad r^2 = r^i r_i. \qquad (5\text{-}25)$$

Equation (24) can be rewritten as

$$A^i = -\frac{1}{4\pi} Q_a \int_{\alpha=-\infty}^{\alpha=+\infty} \frac{da^i/d\alpha}{dr^2/d\alpha}\, \delta(r^2)\, dr^2$$

or, since

$$\frac{dr^2}{d\alpha} = -2r_i a'^i,$$

---

[4] The reader is invited, as an exercise, to deduce the classical definition (3-19) from (23).

as

$$A^i = \frac{1}{8\pi} Q_a \int\limits_{\alpha = -\infty}^{\alpha = +\infty} \frac{a'^i}{r_j a'^j} \delta(r^2)\, dr^2.$$

This is the Liénard–Wiechert formula (3-29), except that it here involves half advanced and half retarded potentials:

$$A^i_{\text{ret, adv}} = \frac{1}{4\pi} Q_a \frac{a'^i}{a'_j r^j_{\text{ret, adv}}} \tag{5-26}$$

$$A^i = \tfrac{1}{2}(A^i_{\text{ret}} + A^i_{\text{adv}}). \tag{5-27}$$

From the formula

$$\partial^i_i \delta(r^2) = -4\pi \left\{ \prod_1^4 \delta(r^i) \right\}$$

proved by Dirac, we conclude, by (23) and (24), that

$$\partial^i_i A^k = j^k. \tag{5-28}$$

We also deduce from (24) that

$$\partial_i A^i = -\frac{1}{4\pi} Q_a [\delta(r^2)]^{\alpha = +\infty}_{\alpha = -\infty} = -\frac{1}{4\pi} Q_a \int\limits_{\alpha = -\infty}^{\alpha = +\infty} d\,[\delta(r^2)] \tag{5-29}$$

and thus the validity of the Lorentz condition for all points a finite distance away, assuming that there are no trajectories $\mathscr{T}$ at infinity.

5.7 Action and Reaction

To simplify both the discussion and the equations, we shall consider the case of only two charges, a and b, denoting the parameters of their two trajectories by α and β, respectively, and their charges by Q_a, Q_b.

Let $A^i_{(a)}$ be the potential created at a by the charge b. If in formula (3-39), here written in the form

$$dP^i_{(a)} = - Q_a \, \partial^i A^l_{(a)} \, da_l,$$

we substitute the expression (24) and note that

$$\partial^i_{(a)} \, \delta(r^2) = - 2\delta'(r^2) r^i$$

(where δ' denotes the derivative of δ with respect to its argument), then we obtain

$$dP^i_{(a)} = - \frac{1}{2\pi} Q_a Q_b \int_{\beta = -\infty}^{\beta = +\infty} \delta'(r^2) r^i \, db^j \, da_j,$$

$$dP^i_{(b)} = + \frac{1}{2\pi} Q_a Q_b \int_{\alpha = -\infty}^{\alpha = +\infty} \delta'(r^2) r^i \, da^j \, db_j.$$

(5-30)

Therefore if, in accordance with Table I on page 89, we liken the combined momentum-energies $P^i_{(a)}$ and $P^i_{(b)}$ to tensions of inextensible filaments $\mathfrak{F}_a$ and $\mathfrak{F}_b$, we see that the interaction of two elements of filament da^i and db^i is proportional to the product of their lengths and to a certain function of their distance apart and of the angles between the three vectors [5] r^i, da^i, db^i. The principle of action and reaction now appears in a form analogous to that of the Biot–Savart law in electromagnetism: the elements of action and reaction create a torque. Note also that the combined momentum-energies P^i are analogous to tensions that are not tangential to the filament and that the space-time forces $r^i \, db^j$ and $r^i \, da^j$ in the integrands are asymmetric tensors.

Note further that, because of the *pseudo*-Euclidean character of space-time, the law of interaction involving $\delta'(r^2)$ is incom-

---

[5] Though Eq. (5-30) involves only the angle between the vectors da^i and db^i, Eq. (5-31) involves the angles between all three vectors.

parably simpler than all those that one could reasonably think of in Euclidean space: each point of a filament is really in interaction with only the two points of the other filament that are "in wave communication" with it. The Wheeler–Feynman action and reaction form a sort of Jacob's ladder by their interlacing of the two main filaments (Fig. 11).

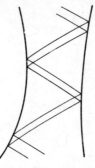

FIG. 11.

Substituting the definition (24) into the expression for the potential momentum-energy

$$p_{(a)}^{*i} = - Q_a A_{(a)}^i ,$$

we obtain

$$dp_{(a)}^{*i} = - \frac{1}{2\pi} Q_a Q_b \int\limits_{\beta = -\infty}^{\beta = +\infty} \delta'(r^2) r^j \, da_j \, db^i .$$

Also we have the identity

$$0 \equiv - \frac{1}{2\pi} Q_a Q_b \, da^i \int\limits_{\beta = -\infty}^{\beta = +\infty} d \, \delta(r^2) = \frac{1}{2\pi} Q_a Q_b \int\limits_{\beta = -\infty}^{\beta = +\infty} \delta'(r^2) r^j \, db_j \, da^i .$$

So, remembering formula (3-40), we deduce from (30) that

$$dp^i_{(a)} = -\frac{1}{2\pi} Q_a Q_b \int\limits_{-\beta=\infty}^{\beta=+\infty}$$

$$\times \delta'(r^2)[(r^i\,db^j - r^j\,db^i)\,da_j - r^j\,db_j\,da^i], \qquad (5\text{-}31)$$

$$dp^i_{(b)} = \frac{1}{2\pi} Q_a Q_b \int\limits_{\alpha=-\infty}^{\alpha=+\infty} \delta'(r^2)[(r^i\,da^j - r^j\,da^i)\,db_j - r^j\,da_j\,db^i].$$

The interpretation of these formulas is analogous to that of (30) (the integrands being equal) but the "tensions" of the filaments are here tangent to the filaments and of constant magnitudes; and correlatively the space-time forces in the integrands, namely $(r^i\,db^j - r^j\,db^i)$ and $(r^i\,da^j - r^j\,da^i)$, have become antisymmetric.

5.8 The Space-Time Coulombian Form of the Interaction Momentum-Energy

Wheeler and Feynman introduced the operator

$$\{\;\} \equiv \left\{ \int\limits_{\alpha}^{+\infty} \int\limits_{-\infty}^{\beta} - \int\limits_{-\infty}^{\alpha} \int\limits_{\beta}^{+\infty} \right\}. \qquad (5\text{-}32)$$

Let us apply it to the two following expressions that enter (30) and (31):

$$(d\alpha, d\beta)^i\,\delta' \equiv \frac{1}{2\pi} Q_a Q_b r^i\,da_j\,db^j\,\delta'(r^2),$$

$$[d\alpha, d\beta]^i\,\delta' \qquad\qquad\qquad\qquad (5\text{-}33)$$

$$\equiv \frac{1}{2\pi} Q_a Q_b [r^i\,da_j\,db^j - r^j(da_j\,db^i + db_j\,da^i)]\,\delta'(r^2).$$

Defining $P^i_{(ab)}$ and $p^i_{(ab)}$ by

$$P^i_{(ab)} = \{ \ \} (d\alpha, \, d\beta)^i \, \delta' \, ,$$
$$p^i_{(ab)} = \{ \ \} [d\alpha, \, d\beta]^i \, \delta' \, , \qquad (5\text{-}34)$$

we find that

$$\frac{\partial}{\partial\alpha} \, P^i_{(ab)} = -\frac{d}{d\alpha} \, P^i_{(a)} \, , \qquad \frac{\partial}{\partial\beta} \, P^i_{(ab)} = \frac{d}{d\beta} \, P^i_{(b)} \, ,$$

$$\frac{\partial}{\partial\alpha} \, p^i_{(ab)} = -\frac{d}{d\alpha} \, p^i_{(a)} \, , \qquad \frac{\partial}{\partial\beta} \, p^i_{(ab)} = \frac{d}{d\beta} \, p^i_{(b)} \, . \qquad (5\text{-}35)$$

In formulating our conclusions, let us return to the general case of n interacting particles. If P^i_0 denotes a constant timelike four-vector defined to within an additive constant and called the *total momentum-energy of the system*, we have the conservation theorem

$$\sum_a P^i_{(a)} + \sum_{a \neq b} P^i_{(ab)} = \sum_a p^i_{(a)} + \sum_{a \neq b} p^i_{(ab)} = P^i_0 \, . \qquad (5\text{-}36)$$

In the second form, where the momenta are tangent to the trajectories, we see that the theorem of the conservation of angular momentum follows as an immediate corollary.

5.9   Fokker's Principle of Stationary Action

The *total action* of the system is defined by the formula

$$\mathscr{A} \equiv \sum_a \int_{-\infty}^{+\infty} p_i \, da^i + \sum_{a \neq b} \frac{1}{2\pi} Q_a Q_b \int_{-\infty}^{+\infty} \int_{-\infty}^{+\infty} \delta \, (r^2) \, da_i \, db^i \, , \qquad (5\text{-}37)$$

which is analogous to that for the total energy in Newtonian mechanics.

If we vary one of the $\mathfrak{F}$, say $\mathfrak{F}_a$, between two fixed point-instants K_1 and K_2, and take account of (24), (3-39), and (3-40), we obtain

$$\delta_a \mathscr{A} = \delta \int_{K_1 K_2} (p^i_{(a)} - Q_a A^i_{(a)})\, da_i = \delta \int_{K_1 K_2} P^i_{(a)}\, da_i = \delta \mathscr{A}_a.$$

Thus it turns out that the variation of the total action with respect to a_i is precisely the variation of the combined action of particle a_i. But by the Hamilton–Jacobi theorem, the equation

$$\delta \mathscr{A}_a = 0$$

is equivalent to the equations of motion of the charge Q_a. Therefore, the equation

$$\delta \mathscr{A} = 0 \tag{5-38}$$

is equivalent to the equations of motion of all the interacting charges.

5.10   The Maxwell Tensor in the Wheeler–Feynman Theory

In the Wheeler–Feynman theory, the Maxwell tensor $\mathscr{M}^{ij}$ given in (3-41) must be calculated using half the sum of the advanced and retarded potentials and suppressing all the squared terms in $Q_a Q_b$. Under these circumstances the integral $\iiint \mathscr{M}^{ij}\, du_j$ will not represent the conserved total momentum-energy but only the interaction momentum-energy, which is not conserved.

If we write symbolically

$$\mathscr{M}^{ij} = (H \cdot H)^{ij}$$

the *Frenkel tensor* is defined by

$$\mathscr{M}^{ij}_F = \sum_{a \neq b} (H_{(a)} \cdot H_{(b)})^{ij}$$

and the *Wheeler–Feynman tensor* by

$$\mathscr{M}^{ij}_{WF} = \sum_{a \neq b} (H_{(a)\mathrm{ret}} \cdot H_{(b)\mathrm{adv}})^{ij}.$$

Wheeler and Feynman have shown that this last definition is precisely the one such that $\iiint \mathcal{M}^{ij} \, du_j$ represents the interaction momentum-energy without an additive constant.

5.11 The Irreversibility of the Radiation According to the Wheeler–Feynman Theory

In his theory of the radiating point electron, Dirac decomposed the total electromagnetic field into the field incident on the particle Q_a and the retarded field created by Q_a:

$$H_{\text{tot}}^{ij} = H_{(a)\text{in}}^{ij} + H_{(a)\text{ret}}^{ij}. \qquad (5\text{-}39)$$

But, wrote Dirac, "We should expect $F_{\text{adv}}^{\mu\nu}$ to play a symmetrical role to $F_{\text{ret}}^{\mu\nu}$ in all questions of general theory," and he therefore wrote

$$H_{\text{tot}}^{ij} = H_{(a)\text{out}}^{ij} + H_{(a)\text{adv}}^{ij}, \qquad (5\text{-}40)$$

where $H_{(a)\text{out}}^{ij}$ denotes the outgoing field of Q_a and, of course, $H_{(a)\text{adv}}^{ij}$ the advanced field created by Q_a. He then defined the radiation field of Q_a by [6]

$$H_{(a)\text{rad}}^{ij} = H_{(a)\text{ret}}^{ij} - H_{(a)\text{adv}}^{ij} = H_{(a)\text{out}}^{ij} - H_{(a)\text{in}}^{ij}. \qquad (5\text{-}41)$$

The field H_{rad}^{ij}, which is a solution of the Maxwell equations without sources, was calculated by Dirac at the point $x_{(a)}^i$, and he found that

$$H_{(a)\text{rad}}^{ij} = \frac{4Q_a}{3c^5} \left[a'''^{i} a'^{j} - a'''^{j} a'^{i} \right], \qquad (5\text{-}42)$$

the derivatives being with respect to the proper time. Then, having subtracted the (infinite) electromagnetic self-momentum-energy, he found as the equations of motion of the particle:

$$p_{(a)}'^{i} = Q H_{(a)}^{ij} a_j', \qquad (5\text{-}43)$$

[6] This is the Jordan–Pauli propagator in quantum field theory.

where
$$H_{(a)}^{ij} = \tfrac{1}{2}\big(H_{(a)\text{in}}^{ij} + H_{(a)\text{out}}^{ij}\big), \tag{5-44}$$

or, in view of the above,

$$H_{(a)}^{ij} = H_{(a)\text{in}}^{ij} + \tfrac{1}{2}H_{(a)\text{rad}}^{ij} = H_{(a)\text{out}}^{ij} - \tfrac{1}{2}H_{(a)\text{rad}}^{ij}. \tag{5-45}$$

Substituting (42) and (45) into (43), noting that $a'^{i}a'_{i} = -c^{2}$, and writing

$$p_{L}'^{i} = \tfrac{1}{2}H_{(a)\text{rad}}^{ij}a'_{j} = -\frac{2Q^{2}}{3c^{3}}\,(a'''^{i} + c^{-2}a'''^{j}a'_{j}a'^{i})$$

$$= -\frac{2Q^{2}}{3c^{3}}\,(a'''^{i} - c^{-2}a''^{j}a''_{j}a'^{i}), \tag{5-46}$$

which is the Lorentz damping force, we obtain

$$p'^{i} = QH_{(a)\text{in}}^{ij}a'_{j} + p_{L}'^{i} = QH_{(a)\text{out}}^{ij}a'_{j} - p_{L}'^{i}. \tag{5-47}$$

The first form is identical to the now-classic expression due to Lorentz; the second belongs to the set of at-first-sight-paradoxical laws of an anti-Carnot universe: a universe in which the motion of the charge Q is described as if it were due to the action of the advanced field absorbed by the other charges and as if it reacted by a Lorentz force with changed sign.

By their theory, Wheeler and Feynman made the ideas of Dirac more concrete. According to them, the exterior field on a^{i} is given by

$$H_{(a)}^{ij} = \tfrac{1}{2}\sum_{b \neq a}\big(H_{(b)\text{ret}}^{ij} + H_{(b)\text{adv}}^{ij}\big), \tag{5-48}$$

which is to be compared with (44). This can also be written

$$H_{(a)}^{ij} = \sum_{b \neq a} H_{(b)\text{ret}}^{ij} + \tfrac{1}{2}\big(H_{(a)\text{ret}}^{ij} - H_{(a)\text{adv}}^{ij}\big) - \tfrac{1}{2}\sum_{\text{all }b}\big(H_{(b)\text{ret}}^{ij} - H_{(b)\text{adv}}^{ij}\big), \tag{5-49}$$

or in a form starting symmetrically with $\sum_{a \neq b} H_{(b)\text{adv}}$.

We recall that Wheeler and Feynman postulate that every emitted photon will ultimately be absorbed and that every absorbed photon was previously emitted. This is a postulate denying the existence of free photons, and it is equivalent to imagining the system under study to be enclosed in an adiabatic enclosure P. From this postulate it follows that

$$\sum_{\text{all } b} (H^{ij}_{(b)\text{ret}} + H^{ij}_{(b)\text{adv}}) = 0 \qquad \text{outside } P,$$

which is possible only if

$$\sum_{\text{all } b} H^{ij}_{(b)\text{ret}} = 0 \quad \text{and} \quad \sum_{\text{all } b} H^{ij}_{(b)\text{adv}} = 0 \qquad \text{outside } P,$$

whence

$$\sum_{\text{all } b} (H^{ij}_{(b)\text{ret}} - H^{ij}_{(b)\text{adv}}) = 0 \qquad \text{outside } P.$$

But since the last field is a solution of the Maxwell equations without sources, this relation can hold only if

$$\sum_{\text{all } b} (H^{ij}_{(b)\text{ret}} - H^{ij}_{(b)\text{adv}}) \equiv 0. \tag{5-50}$$

On comparing the Dirac equations (45) and (41), respectively with the Wheeler–Feynman equations (49) and (50), we obtain, as expected, the identification (48).

Thus the most striking result of this highly ingenious theory of Wheeler and Feynman is the appearance of a paradox in radiation theory that is closely analogous to that of Loschmidt in statistical mechanics, where the system under study is also assumed to be adiabatically isolated. How can we reconcile the experimental irreversibility of phenomena with the perfect symmetry between past and future of the fundamental physical equations and their consequences? This is a fascinating and important question, but to discuss it here would take us too far from our main topic.[7]

---

[7] In recent years, the problem of irreversibility has been the subject of extremely interesting investigations by physicists (Watanabe, E. N. Adams, J. A. McLennan, Wu and Rivier, Penrose and Percival) and by philosophers (H. Reichenbach, A. Grünbaum, H. Mehlberg). We summarized all these studies, as well as our own, in Proceedings of the 1964 Jerusalem Congress on Methodology, North-Holland Publ., Amsterdam, 1965.

C. Wave Mechanics in the Geometrical Approximation (Louis de Broglie [8])

5.12 Relativistic Formulation of Geometrical Optics

Consider a complex scalar function of a point-instant

$$\varphi(x) = \rho(x) e^{i\alpha(x)}. \qquad (5\text{-}51)$$

The geometrical approximation of wave mechanics consists in assuming that $\varphi(x)$ determines certain physical properties by the values of its argument α alone.

These properties clearly repeat themselves when α changes by $2n\pi$, where n is an integer. The three-dimensional hypersurfaces $\mathscr{A}$ given by

$$\alpha(x) = \text{const} \qquad (5\text{-}52)$$

will be called wave surfaces, or phase surfaces. The identity

$$d\alpha = \partial_i \alpha \, dx^i \qquad (5\text{-}53)$$

shows the physical significance of the four-vector

$$k_i = \partial_i \alpha : \qquad (5\text{-}54)$$

since $k_i \, dx^i / 2\pi$ is the number of equiphase surfaces cutting the vector dx^i, the quantity $k_i/2\pi$ is the *spatio-temporal frequency four-vector*. Introducing the direction cosines α^u of the spatial projection k of k_i, let us rewrite formulas (2-33) ($u=1, 2, 3$), namely

$$k^u = \frac{2\pi}{L} \alpha^u \quad \text{and} \quad k^4 = \frac{2\pi i}{cT}, \quad \text{with} \quad \alpha^u \alpha_u = 1 , \quad (5\text{-}55)$$

but this time with

$$L = wT , \qquad w \neq c . \qquad (5\text{-}56)$$

---

[8] Recherches sur la Théorie des Quanta. *Ann. Phys., Paris*, **3**, 22 (1925); reprinted by Masson, Paris, 1963. Proceedings published by North-Holland Publ., Amsterdam, 1965.

If we now write

$$w = w\alpha \qquad \text{or} \qquad \alpha_u = \frac{1}{w} w_u, \qquad (5\text{-}57)$$

we see by (55) that

$$\frac{c}{w^2} w_u = \frac{i}{k_4} k_u. \qquad (5\text{-}58)$$

The orthogonal trajectories $\mathscr{R}$ of the hypersurfaces $\mathscr{A}$ are, by definition, the *rays* of geometrical optics. We shall see that they are timelike for the motion of a free particle, though this is not the case in general if the particle moves in an exterior field. In any case, we write

$$v_u = \frac{ic}{k_4} k_u, \qquad (5\text{-}59)$$

this definition coinciding with that of the kinematical velocity when the rays $\mathscr{R}$ are timelike.

Formulas (58) and (59) show that the two vectors v and w are collinear, and that their magnitudes are related as follows:

$$\alpha = \frac{v}{v} = \frac{w}{w}, \qquad \text{or} \qquad v \cdot w = vw = c^2. \qquad (5\text{-}60)$$

DE BROGLIE'S GROUP-VELOCITY THEOREM. At each point-instant let the four-vector k^i undergo a small dispersion δk^i that does not alter its length:

$$k^i \, \delta k_i = 0. \qquad (5\text{-}61)$$

By (53) and (54), the phase difference, $d\alpha$, associated with the interval dx^i separating two *fixed* point-instants will then undergo a variation

$$\delta \, d\alpha = \delta k^i \, dx_i. \qquad (5\text{-}62)$$

The necessary and sufficient condition for $\delta \, d\alpha$ to be zero is evidently that dx_i be orthogonal to $\mathscr{A}$, and this shows that v is the *group velocity* of the waves, which is always less than c in the case of free particles. The speeds v, w of the phase and group waves, respectively, are related by the universal formula $vw = c^2$ (see (60)).

We recognize in the group-velocity theorem of Louis de Broglie the four-dimensional extension of Fresnel's theorem of stationary phase, according to which the principal contribution to the illumination at a point P caused by a source S is due to a small packet of waves whose mean direction coincides with that of SP.

5.13 De Broglie's Wave Mechanics

The formal parallelism between geometrical optics and the analytical mechanics of a particle had not escaped the great classical workers, Hamilton,[9] Klein,[10] and Vessiot.[11]

We can summarize it in a table of correspondences (Table II):

TABLE II
CORRESPONDENCE BETWEEN THE ANALYTICAL MECHANICS OF A PARTICLE AND GEOMETRICAL OPTICS

Hamilton–Jacobi surfaces	Wave surfaces
Pencils of virtual trajectories	Pencils of rays
Maupertuis–Hamilton extremal theorems	Fermat extremal theorem

Before relativity and wave mechanics, one point had been obscure: the speed of the particle appears in the numerator of

[9] *Trans. Roy. Irish Acad.* **15**, 79 (1858); and *Dublin Univ. Rev.* (1833).
[10] *Jahresb. Deutsch. Math. Ver.* **1**, 230 (1906).
[11] *Ann. Ecole Norm. Supérieure*, p. 134 (1909).

the Maupertuis–Hamilton formula of stationary action, but the phase speed of the waves appears in the denominator of Fermat's formula. De Broglie's group-velocity theorem removes the difficulty since, because of (60), the group speed of the waves will be in the numerator of the Fermat formula.

But by introducing the periodicity of the phase, de Broglie was able to take a further important step.

In quantized dynamics, the action $\mathscr{A}$ occurs as integral multiples of Planck's constant h ($h = 6.626 \times 10^{-27}$ erg sec) while in optics the phase is measured in units of 2π. This suggested to de Broglie the idea of physically identifying particle dynamics with a generalized optics by writing

$$\mathscr{A} = h\alpha, \qquad \hbar \equiv \frac{h}{2\pi}, \tag{5-63}$$

so that, by (5-2),

$$P^i \equiv p^i - QA^i = \hbar k^i, \qquad cm_0 = \hbar k_0, \tag{5-64}$$

where k_0 denotes the length of the vector k^i.

The Hamilton–Jacobi equation (5-19) then becomes

$$(\partial^i \alpha + \varepsilon A^i)(\partial_i \alpha + \varepsilon A_i) = -k_0^2, \tag{5-65}$$

with

$$\varepsilon = \frac{Q}{\hbar}. \tag{5-66}$$

In the geometrical approximation, this is the equation of the waves associated with charged particles of zero spin (π^+ or π^- mesons, for example).

For free particles with or without spin the wave equation, in the geometrical approximation, is

$$\partial^i \alpha \, \partial_i \alpha + k_0^2 = 0 \tag{5-67}$$

and this shows that the wave mechanics of a free particle is, formally, a four-dimensional extension of the classical theory of diffraction in the purely monochromatic case. The significance of condition (61) becomes clear in this context: it is the condition of "four-dimensional monochromaticity," i.e., of conservation of the proper frequency k_0 and of the proper mass m_0.

Finally, de Broglie completed the Hamilton–Jacobi table of correspondences as shown in Table III.

TABLE III

DE BROGLIE'S COMPLETION OF TABLE II

Combined action	Phase
Combined momentum-energy P^i	Four-frequency k^i
Proper mass m_0	Proper frequency k_0

5.14   Transition to Wave Mechanics: the de Broglie–Klein–Gordon Equation

As in classical optics, the "wave" analog of the "geometrical" equation (67) is

$$(\partial_i^i - k_0^2)\varphi(x) \equiv (\square - k_0^2)\varphi(x) = 0. \qquad (5\text{-}68)$$

Substituting (51) into (68), we find:

$$\partial^i\alpha\,\partial_i\alpha + k_0^2 = \frac{1}{\rho}\partial_i^i\rho, \qquad (5\text{-}69)$$

$$\partial_i^i\alpha = -\frac{2}{\rho}\,\partial^i\rho\,\partial_i\alpha. \qquad (5\text{-}70)$$

If, then, we make the approximations

$$\frac{1}{\rho}\partial^i\rho \sim 0, \qquad \frac{1}{\rho}\partial_i^i\rho \sim 0, \qquad (5\text{-}71)$$

we obtain the Hamilton–Jacobi equation (67) completed by the condition

$$\partial_i^i \alpha = 0. \tag{5-72}$$

These two equations are satisfied by monochromatic plane waves:

$$\varphi(x) = \theta(k) \exp[\mathrm{i}k^i x_i], \tag{5-73}$$

with

$$k^i k_i + k_0^2 = 0. \tag{5-74}$$

5.15 Epilogue

De Broglie's 1925 wave mechanics has as its spiritual heir the 1946–1950 quantum field theory in its relativistically covariant form.

By revealing the presence of waves at the very heart of dynamics, as Einstein had revealed their presence at the heart of kinematics, Louis de Broglie has shown us that, in a profound sense, relativity and quantum theory, those two great achievements of modern physics, are kin.

Bibliography

(Works in English)

J. Aharoni, "The Special Theory of Relativity," Oxford Univ. Press, London and New York, 1959.

P. G. Bergmann, The Special Theory of Relativity, in "Handbuch der Physik" (S. Flügge, ed.), vol. 4, pp. 109–193. Springer, Berlin and New York, 1962.

P. W. Bridgman, "A Sophisticate's Primer of Relativity," Wesleyan Univ. Press, Middleton, Connecticut, 1962.

A. D. Fokker, "Time and Space, Weight and Inertia." Pergamon Press, Oxford, 1965.

R. Hagedorn, "Relativistic Kinematics." Benjamin, New York and Amsterdam, 1963.

C. Møller, "The Theory of Relativity," Oxford Univ. Press, London and New York, 1952.

W. Pauli, "Theory of Relativity" (translated by G. Field), Pergamon Press, Oxford, 1958.

W. Rindler, "Special Relativity," Oliver & Boyd, Edinburgh (2nd. edition, 1966), and Wiley (Interscience), New York, 1966.

J. L. Synge, "Relativity: The Special Theory," North-Holland Publ., Amsterdam [Wiley (Interscience), New York], 1956.

H. Weyl, "Space, Time, and Matter" (translated by H. L. Brose), Dover, New York, 1922.

NAME INDEX

SUBJECT INDEX